PROBLEMS

❖

NUMBER ONE

New Problems in Euclidean Geometry

David Monk

The United Kingdom Mathematics Trust

New Problems in Euclidean Geometry

Published by The United Kingdom Mathematics Trust.

Maths Challenges Office, School of Mathematics, University of Leeds, Leeds, LS2 9JT, United Kingdom

http://www.ukmt.org.uk

First published 2009.

ISBN 978-1-906001-09-4

Printed in the UK for the UKMT by The Charlesworth Group, Wakefield.
http://www.charlesworth.com

Typographic design by Andrew Jobbings of Arbelos.
http://www.arbelos.co.uk

Typeset with LaTeX.

The books published by the United Kingdom Mathematics Trust are grouped into series.

The EXCURSIONS IN MATHEMATICS series consists of monographs which focus on a particular topic of interest and investigate it in some detail, using a wide range of ideas and techniques. They are aimed at high school students, undergraduates and others who are prepared to pursue a subject in some depth, but do not require specialised knowledge.

1. *The Backbone of Pascal's Triangle*, Martin Griffiths

The HANDBOOKS series is aimed particularly at students at secondary school who are interested in acquiring the knowledge and skills which are useful for tackling challenging problems, such as those posed in the competitions administered by the UKMT and similar organisations.

1. *Plane Euclidean Geometry: Theory and Problems*, A D Gardiner and C J Bradley

2. *Introductions to Number Theory and Inequalities*, C J Bradley

3. *A Mathematical Olympiad Primer*, Geoff C Smith

The PATHWAYS series aims to provide classroom teaching material for use in secondary schools. Each title develops a subject in more depth and in more detail than is normally required by public examinations or national curricula.

1. *Crossing the Bridge*, Gerry Leversha

The PROBLEMS series consists of collections of high-quality and original problems of Olympiad standard.

1. *New Problems in Euclidean Geometry*, David Monk

The YEARBOOKS series documents all the UKMT activities, including details of all the challenge papers and solutions, lists of high scorers, accounts of the IMO and Olympiad training camps, and other information about the Trust's work during each year.

Contents

Series Editor's Foreword

New Problems in Euclidean Geometry should appeal to anyone who enjoys solving the kind of challenging and attractive geometry problems that have virtually vanished from the school curriculum, but which still play a central role in national and international mathematics competitions. As well as the questions themselves, it contains useful hints for their solution as well as suggestions for further reading.

This book is the first one in what I hope will be a series of collections of high-quality and original problems of Olympiad standard.

London, UK   GERRY LEVERSHA

About the author

The name of David Monk is legendary among those involved in Mathematical Olympiads. For over forty years he has made major contributions to the Olympiad scene, a fact that was recognised publicly in September 2008 by the presentation of a gold medal at an event held in The Royal Society.

It has been my privilege to know David even longer. He was the first person to lecture to me as an undergraduate at the University of Edinburgh in October 1964. By the end of the first week we were immersed in the AM/GM inequality and the first appearance of epsilon followed very soon after. It was clear to all of us that we were in the presence of a master.

Not long after, in 1967, the UK took part for the first time in the International Mathematical Olympiad (IMO) . David was involved right from the start, serving as Deputy Leader in 1968. He acted as either Leader or Deputy Leader on 10 occasions, the last being as Leader in 1989. I was delighted to have him as a colleague on the Jury and Problem Selection Committee when the IMO was held in Glasgow in 2002.

Training students for Olympiads requires a plentiful supply of problems of appropriate difficulty. David must rate as one of the finest composers of such problems in the world. Indeed he holds the record of having had no fewer than fourteen of his creations used in IMO papers (so far!), six more than his nearest rival. Many more have been used to prepare students in the art of solving hard problems. Indeed, David ran a number of correspondence courses on problem solving nearly 30 years ago, where ideas of his own took their place alongside gems from elsewhere.

David has always been very self-effacing about his extraordinary gift of problem creation; he would worry that perhaps a problem was not original. We shall never know for certain the provenance of many things in Mathematics. One thing that is certain is that in this book we have a treasure trove of wonderful problems. Students the world over will have the chance to tackle them and to marvel at their beauty, as well as at the ingenuity of their creator.

On behalf of all his many friends, I should like to congratulate David on a magnificent lifetime achievement and extend to him our very best wishes for the future.

Glasgow, UK   ADAM MCBRIDE

Preface

This collection of geometrical problems consists of material accumulated over many years. It stems from my long involvement with the organisation of, and training teams for, Mathematical Olympiads—work that has given me much interest and enjoyment. The great majority of the problems were composed by me, either as a result of my explorations or occasionally by modifying other problems. However, because of the lapse of time and the rather unsystematic nature of my notes, it is possible that a few items from other sources have crept in. A small number have been used in, or proposed for, competitions. It is in any case impossible, in a topic with such widespread and historical literature, to be sure that ideas have not appeared independently elsewhere. Be that as it may, I hope the collection will be found interesting and helpful.

The problems have been roughly divided into five categories:

E	Easy
M	Moderate difficulty
H	Hard
C	Computational
T	Trigonometrical

The first three of these contain easy, moderate and hard problems which are approachable by mainly Euclidean methods. The last two consist of problems which require a lot of trigonometry. In the first four categories, the problems are accompanied by diagrams, with a single problem on a page. The problems in category **T** are presented without any diagrams. Note that in the problems with an accompanying diagram, sometimes there are two possible answers, but only one of the two cases is illustrated.

Some hints and notes are provided, but not full solutions. The hints generally involve only elementary ideas. Occasionally, though, more advanced concepts are mentioned, such as isogonal conjugate or harmonic range. The Glossary at the end of the book includes a list of definitions and standard results which might prove to be useful.

With regard to the diagrams two important comments must be made. The printed figure should not be used as a substitute for one's own diagram when tackling a problem—drawing a figure for oneself is a significant help in getting a 'feel' for a configuration. Secondly, accurate figures such as these can indicate concurrences and other aspects of the situation which must not be assumed without proof! A few instances of this are mentioned in the hints.

In many cases the methods of solution suggested are computational, using trigonometry or coordinates. Of course, in mathematical contests any correct approach, even using a combination of techniques, is acceptable. For the connoisseur, however, the traditional Euclidean method occupies the high ground. So this collection presents a challenge: to find such a proof where this is feasible and none is suggested in the hint.

I am extremely grateful to Christopher Bradley who encouraged me to publish this collection and with whom I have enjoyed correspondence on geometry for many years. He provided an initial version of the typescript which was the basis for much preliminary work. He has also contributed substantially to the hints, but the ultimate responsibility for the problems rests with me.

I should add my appreciation of the many friendships made over the years I have been associated with Olympiad activities. I cannot name everybody but special thanks are also due to Adam McBride and Bill Richardson for their support for this book, and to James Gazet and Gerry Leversha for their highly efficient editorial work.

Edinburgh, UK   DAVID MONK

Chapter 1

Problems E

Problem E 1

In triangle ABC the midpoints of the sides are denoted by L, M, N.

Prove that $\angle LAC = \angle ABM$ if, and only if, $\angle ANC = \angle ALB$.

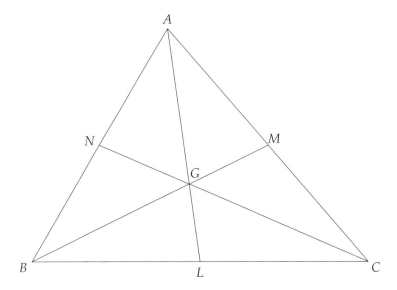

Problem E 2

The tangents at A, B to circle ABC meet at T. The line through T parallel to AC meets BC at D.

Prove that $AD = CD$.

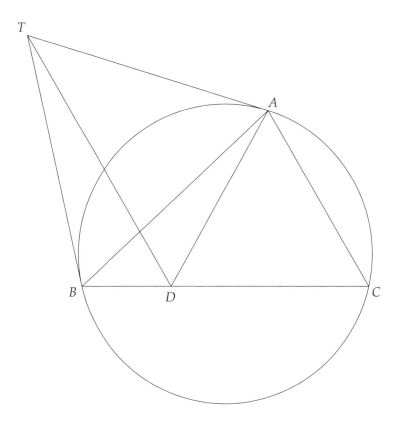

Problem E 3

In the cyclic quadrilateral $ABCD$ the point E is the midpoint of BC. The perpendicular to BC at E meets the line AB at X and the perpendicular from E to AD meets the line CD at Y.

Prove that XY is perpendicular to CD.

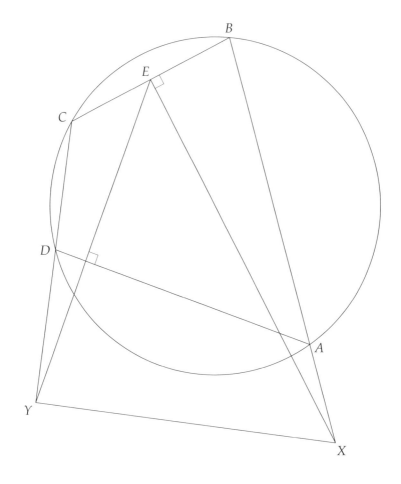

Problem E 4

The quadrilateral $ABCD$ is cyclic. The perpendicular bisector of CD meets AD at P and BD at Q.

Prove that $\angle ACQ = \angle PCB$.

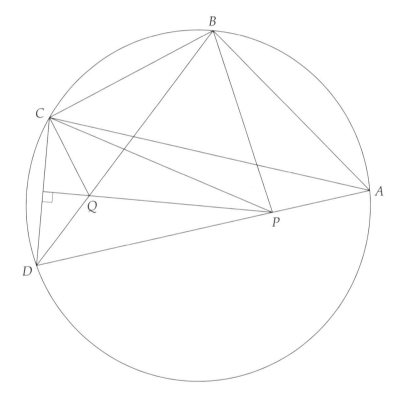

Problem E 5

In the convex quadrilateral $ABCD$ the side AB is not parallel to CD. Its diagonals AC and BD meet at O. The parallel through O to AB meets AD at P and BC at Q; the parallel through O to CD meets BC at T and AD at U.

Show that if $PO \times OQ = TO \times OU$ then $ABCD$ is cyclic.

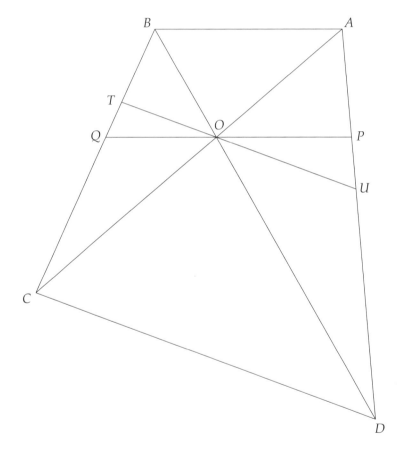

Problem E 6

Let ABC be a triangle with orthocentre H and let P be a point on its circumcircle. The line through A parallel to BP meets CH at Q and the line through A parallel to CP meets BH at R.

Prove that QR is parallel to AP.

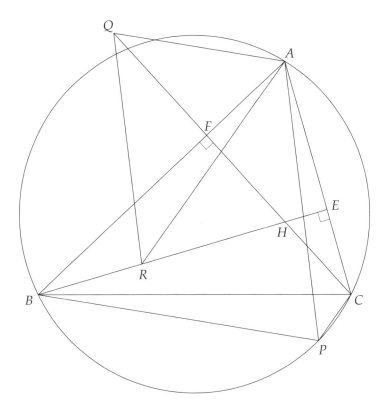

Problem E 7

The acute-angled triangle ABC has circumcentre O. Points P on AC (extended beyond C, if necessary) and Q on BA (extended beyond A, if necessary) are chosen so that triangles BPQ and ABC are similar, with vertices corresponding as listed.

Prove that O is the orthocentre of triangle BPQ.

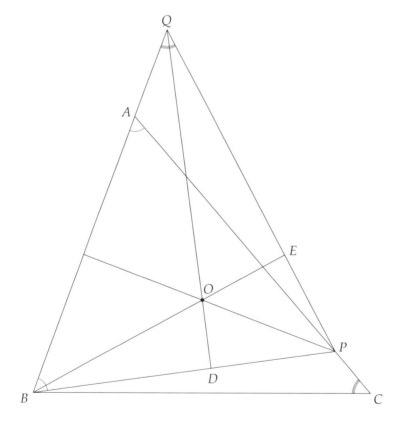

Problem E 8

The triangle ABC is not isosceles. The points O and H are its circumcentre and orthocentre, respectively, and M is the midpoint of OH.

(a) If ABC is acute-angled and the internal bisector of $\angle BAC$ passes through M, calculate $\angle BAC$.

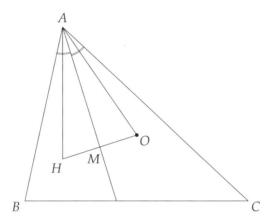

(b) If ABC is obtuse-angled and the external bisector of $\angle BAC$ passes through M, calculate $\angle BAC$.

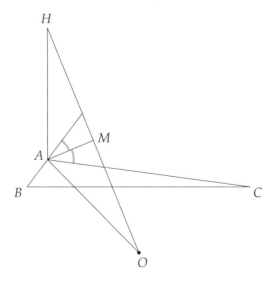

Problem E 9

The inscribed circle of triangle ABC has centre I and touches CA at P and AB at Q. The lines BI and CI meet the line PQ at X and Y, respectively.

Prove that X, Y, B, C are concyclic and identify the centre of this circle.

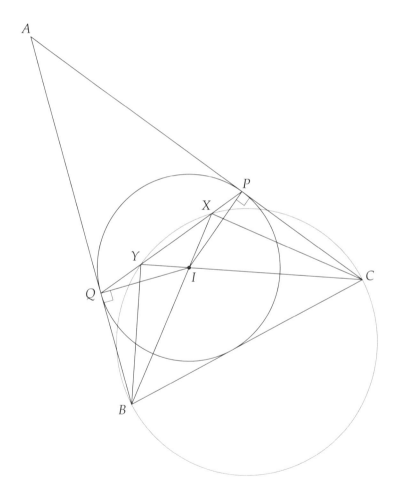

Problem E 10

In parallelogram $ABCD$, the point H is the orthocentre of triangle ABC. The line through H parallel to AB meets BC at P and AD at Q; the line through H parallel to BC meets AB at R and CD at S.

Prove that P, Q, R, S lie on a circle.

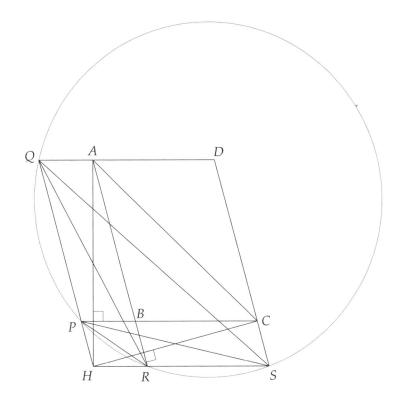

Problem E 11

For any point P inside triangle ABC, let D, E, F be the feet of the perpendiculars from P onto BC, CA, AB, respectively.

Show that

$$\frac{EF \times PD}{AP} + \frac{FD \times PE}{BP} + \frac{DE \times PF}{CP}$$

is independent of P.

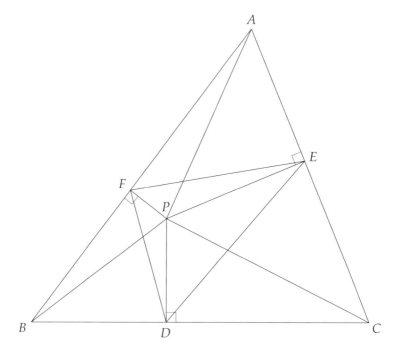

Problem E 12

The point A does not lie on the circle C. The lines joining A to the vertices P, Q, R of a variable equilateral triangle inscribed in C meet C again at U, V, W, respectively.

Prove that

$$\frac{AP}{AU} + \frac{AQ}{AV} + \frac{AR}{AW}$$

is constant.

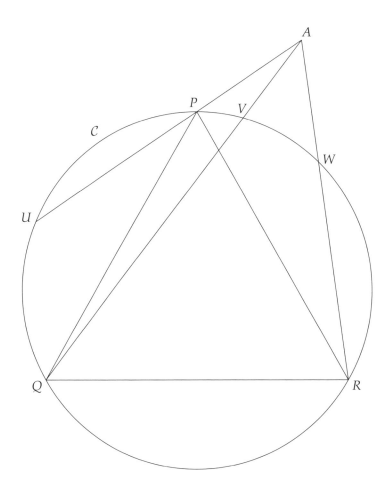

Problem E 13

The parallelogram $PQRS$ is not a rectangle. The lines a, b, c are drawn perpendicular to PQ, PR, PS at Q, R, S, respectively, and form a triangle with A the intersection of b, c, and so on.

Prove that P is the intersection of the tangents at A and C to the circumcircle of ABC.

If $[ABC] = 2[PQRS]$, find the magnitude of $\angle ABC$.

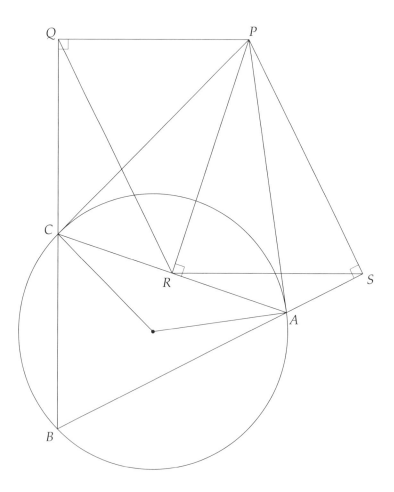

Problem E 14

In the quadrilateral $ABCD$ the diagonals AC and BD meet at R. The sides AB and DC produced meet at Q.

Prove that if $ABCD$ is cyclic then

$$\frac{AR \times AC}{AQ} = \frac{BR \times BD}{BQ}.$$

Is the converse true?

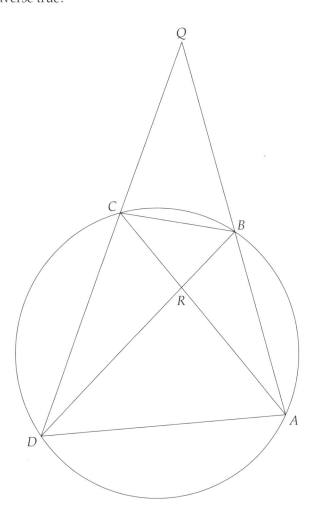

Problem E 15

The quadrilateral $ABCD$ is cyclic. The sides AD and BC meet at P; the diagonals AC and BD meet at R. The points X, Y, Z are the feet of the perpendiculars from D to AC, BC, PR.

Prove that the circle XYZ passes through the midpoint M of CD.

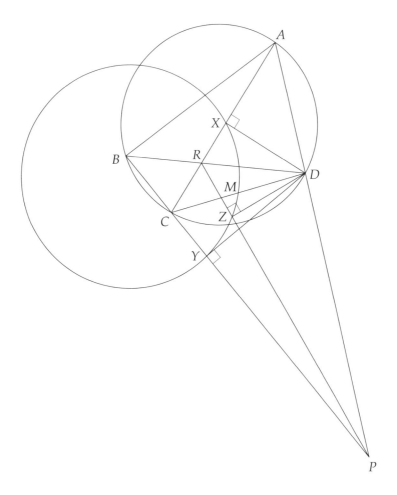

Problem E 16

The points L, M, N are the midpoints of the sides BC, CA, AB of triangle ABC. The points P and Q are on AB and BC, respectively; R and S are points such that N is the midpoint of PR and L is the midpoint of QS.

Prove that if PS and QR meet at right angles at T, then T lies on circle LMN.

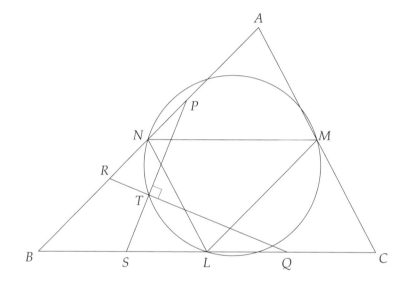

Problem E 17

The point D is on the circumcircle of the equilateral triangle ABC. The lines AD, BD, CD meet BC, CA, AB at P, Q, R, respectively. The circle with centre D and radius DP meets BC again at X. Points Y, Z are similarly defined on CA, AB, respectively.

Prove that X, Y, Z are collinear.

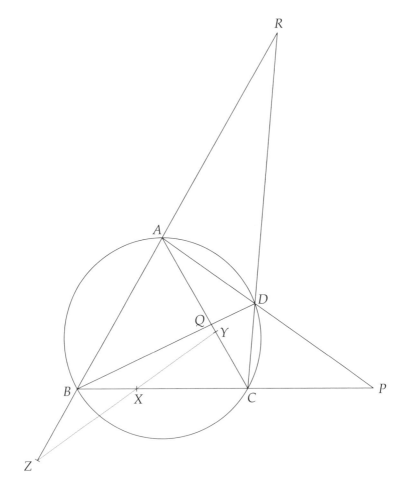

Problem E 18

The triangle ABC is acute-angled. The circle through A touching BC at B and the circle through A touching BC at C meet again at U.

Given that the circle through U touching AB at B and the circle through U touching AC at C have a common tangent at U find $\angle BAC$.

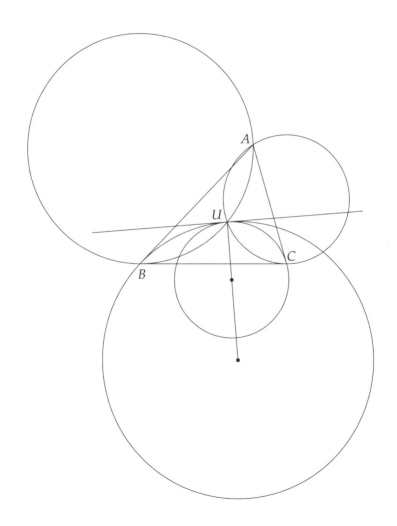

Chapter 2

Problems M

Problem M 1

In triangle ABC with AB and AC unequal, the point D is the foot of the perpendicular from A to BC, the points E and F are the midpoints of AD and BC, respectively, and G is the foot of the perpendicular from B to AF.

Prove that EF is the tangent at F to the circle GFC.

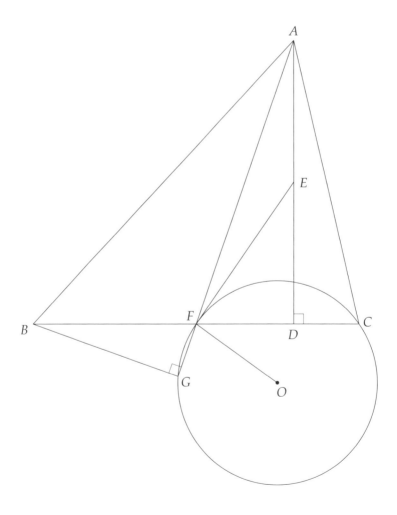

Problem M 2

The circles C and C^* lie in a plane and meet at two distinct points. Consider points P with the following property:

(*) *If T is a point of contact of a tangent from P to C and if circle S_P with centre P and radius PT meets C^* at Q, Q^*, then QQ^* passes through P.*

Show that points P with property (*) exist and that they all lie on a circle K.

Prove also that K contains all points which satisfy the condition (*) with the roles of C and C^* interchanged.

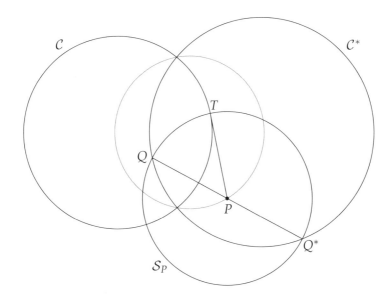

Problem M 3

Given a parallelogram $ABCD$, let E be the point diametrically opposite to B on the circle ABC.

Prove that the circles ADE and ABC have equal radii.

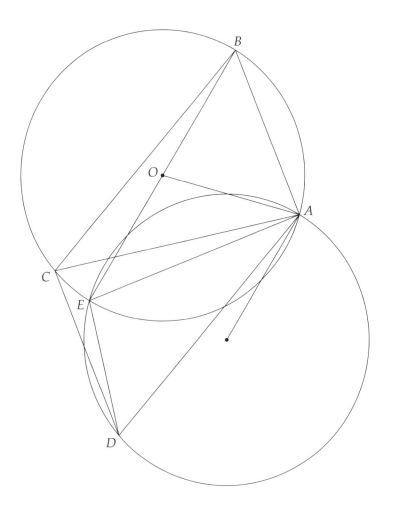

Problem M 4

Through the midpoint L of side BC of triangle ABC (in which $AC \neq 3AB$) a line is drawn parallel to the internal bisector of $\angle BAC$, meeting the lines AB and AC at X and Y, respectively. The line XY is extended to Z so that $XY = YZ$. The lines BY and CZ meet at D.

Prove that the internal bisector of $\angle BDC$ is parallel to XY.

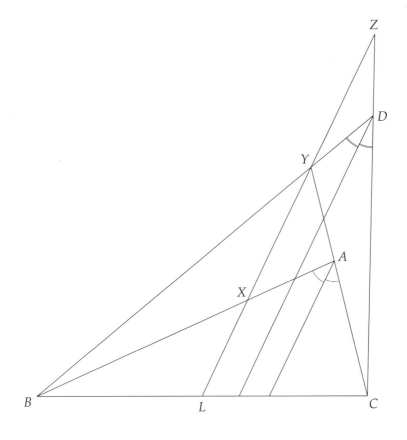

Problem M 5

In triangle ABC, the points L and M are the midpoints of BC and CA, respectively, and CF is the altitude from C. The circle through A and M which has AL as its tangent at A meets the extension of BA at X.

Find the minimum value of $\dfrac{BX}{CF}$ and specify the triangles ABC for which the minimum is obtained.

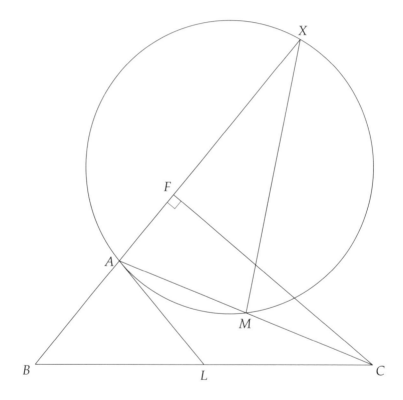

Problem M 6

The triangle ABC has circumcentre O and orthocentre H. The line OA is extended to O' so that $OA = AO'$; the midpoint of AH is H'. The tangent at A to the circumcircle meets the line BC at T.

Prove that A, O, T, H' are concyclic.

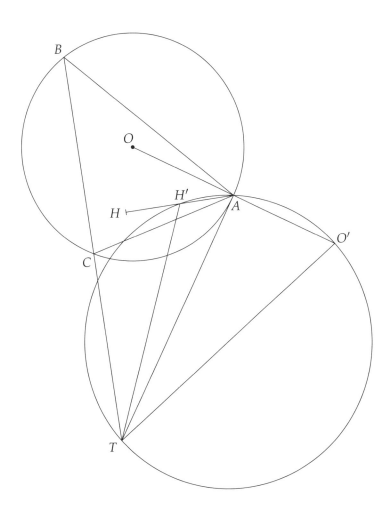

Problem M 7

The point A is on a circle with centre O. The line OA is extended to C so that $OA = AC$, and B is the midpoint of AC. The point Q is on the circle such that $\angle AOQ$ is obtuse. The line QO meets the perpendicular bisector of CQ at P.

Prove that $\angle POB = 2\angle PBO$.

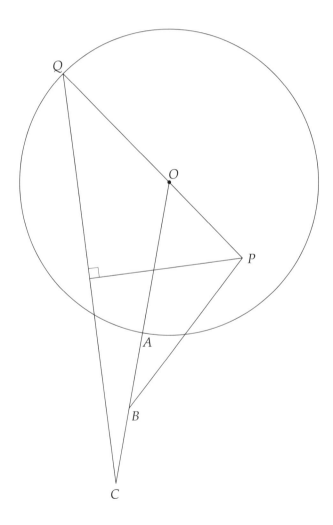

Problem M 8

A circle has diameter AB. The tangents at A and B are ℓ and m, respectively. The tangent at a further point P meets ℓ at S and m at W. The join of P to the midpoint U of AS meets m at V and the circle again at Q. The tangent at Q meets m at T, and the perpendicular at Q to PQ meets AB at X.

Find the ratios $BV : BT$, $BW : BT$ and $AX : AB$.

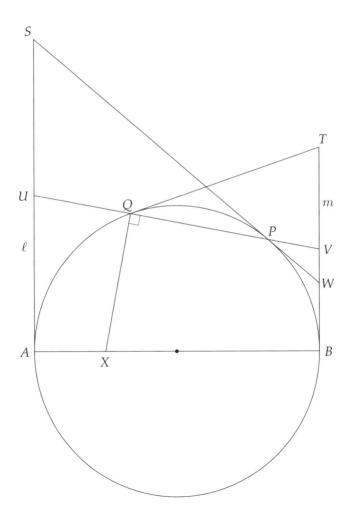

Problem M 9

The point P lies on the internal bisector of $\angle BAC$. The point D is the midpoint of BC and PD meets the external bisector of $\angle BAC$ at E.

Prove that if F is the point such that $PAEF$ is a rectangle then PF bisects (internally or externally) $\angle BFC$.

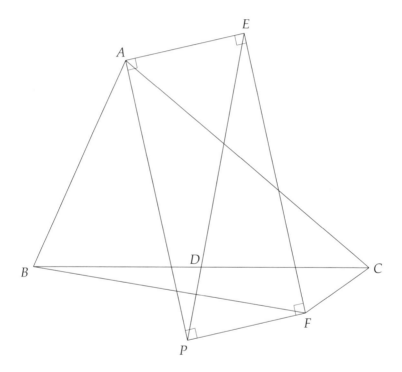

Problem M 10

The tangents at A and B to the circumcircle of triangle ABC meet at T. The circle ABT meets BC, AC again at D, E respectively, and CT meets BE at F.

Given that D is the midpoint of BC find the ratio $BF : FE$.

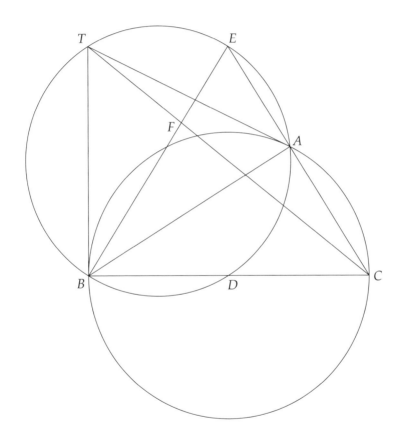

Problem M 11

In the quadrilateral $ABCD$, the perpendicular from A to BD meets the perpendicular from B to CD at P; the perpendicular from C to BD meets the perpendicular from D to AB at Q.

Prove that PQ passes through the point of intersection of the diagonals AC and BD.

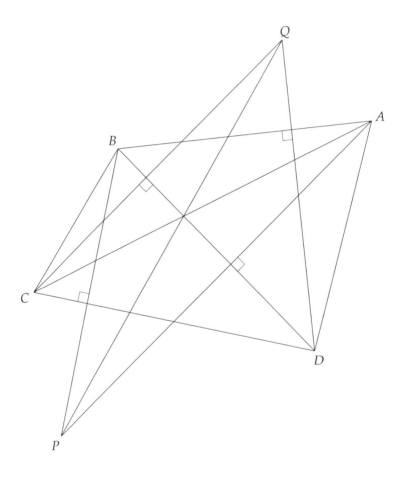

Problem M 12

The quadrilateral $ABCD$ is cyclic. The lines AB and DC produced meet at Q. The lines DA and CB produced meet at P. The midpoints of the diagonals AC and BD are L and M respectively; the point K is the orthocentre of triangle MPQ.

(a) Prove that P, Q, K, L lie on a circle.

(b) Prove that $\angle PML = \angle LKQ$.

(c) Prove that $\angle KLM = 90°$.

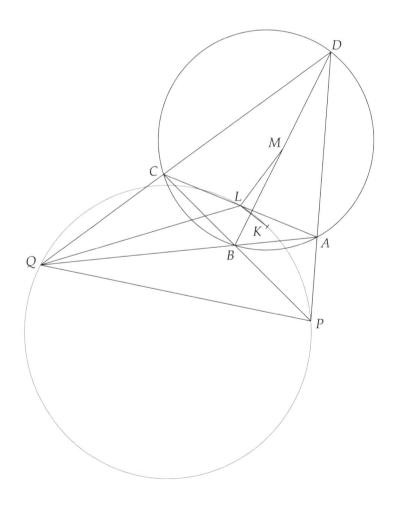

Problem M 13

The quadrilateral $ABCD$ is cyclic. The extensions of the lines AD and BC meet at X; those of AB and CD meet at Y. The lines AC and BD meet XY at P and Q respectively. The midpoints of AC and BD are E and F respectively.

Prove that E, F, P, Q are concyclic.

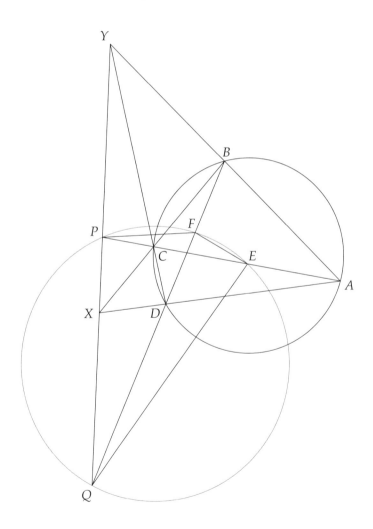

Problem M 14

The quadrilateral $ABCD$ is cyclic. The sides AD and BC produced meet at P; the sides AB and DC produced meet at Q.

Prove that if $\angle APQ = 90°$ then the perpendicular from P to AB passes through the midpoint M of the diagonal BD.

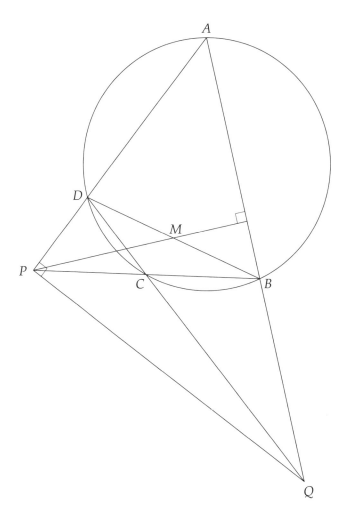

Problem M 15

The quadrilateral $ABCD$ is cyclic. The line through D parallel to BC meets CA at P, AB at Q and the circle again at R. The line through D parallel to AB meets CA at S, BC at T and the circle again at U.

Prove that if $PQ = QR$ then $ST = TU$.

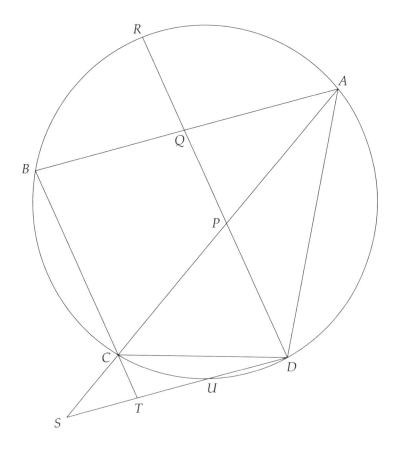

Problem M 16

The quadrilateral $ABCD$ is inscribed in a circle with centre O. The extensions of the sides AD, BC meet at P and those of BA, CD meet at Q. The line through Q perpendicular to AC meets OP at X.

Prove that $\angle ABX = 90°$.

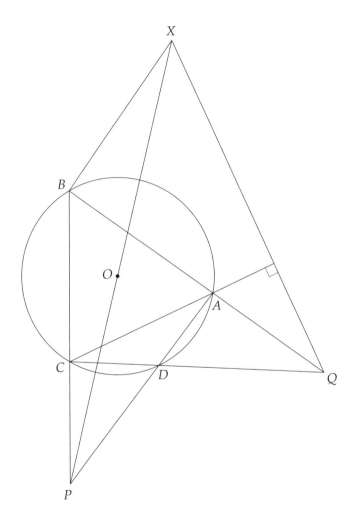

Problem M 17

In the quadrilateral $ABCD$, the perpendicular bisector of AB meets the line AD at X; the perpendicular bisector of CD meets the line BC at Y.

Prove that if $ABCD$ is cyclic then XY is parallel to AC.

Is the converse true: if XY is parallel to AC is $ABCD$ necessarily cyclic?

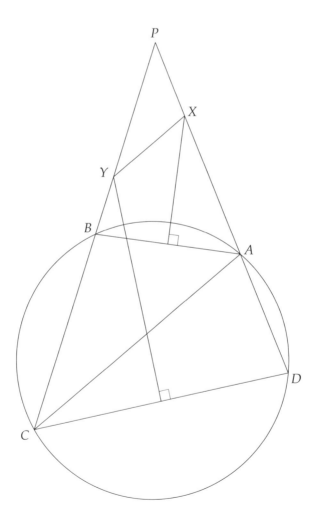

Problem M 18

Four distinct points are given on a circle with centre O.

Prove that *in general* there exist two lines ℓ, m through O with the following property:

For every choice of two of the four points, if the line k joining these meets ℓ at P and the join of the other two points meets m at Q, then PQ is perpendicular to k.

Consider what exceptional cases can arise.

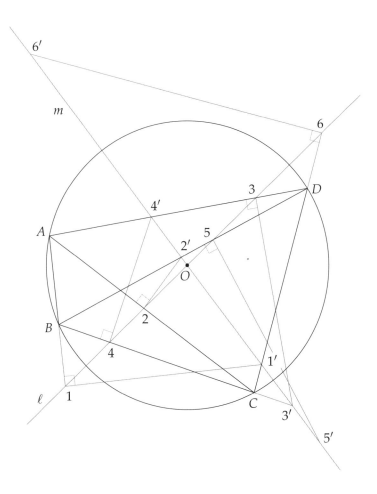

Problem M 19

The triangle ABC is acute-angled. The perpendicular bisectors of AB and CA meet the median through A at W and V, respectively. The lines CV and BW meet at T. The point U is the intersection of AVW with the circumcircle of ABC.

(a) Prove that $AT^2 = BT \times CT$.

(b) Prove that $AU = BT + CT$.

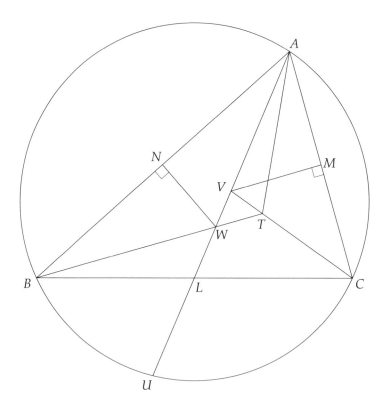

Problem M 20

The tangents at B, C to circle ABC meet at T. The points L, M, N are the midpoints of BC, CA, AB, respectively. The lines AT and NL meet at X; the lines AT and LM meet at Y.

Prove that BX is parallel to CY.

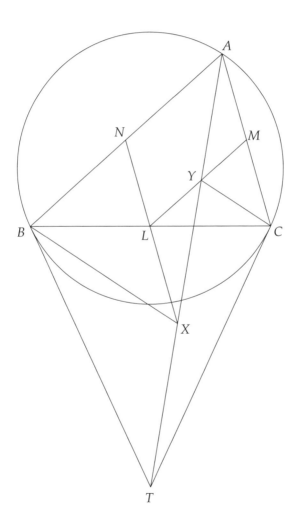

Chapter 3

Problems H

Problem H 1

The altitudes BE and CF of a triangle ABC meet at H. The extensions of FE and BC meet at U. A line through the midpoint L of BC parallel to the internal bisector of $\angle EUB$ meets CA, AB, HC, HB (extended as necessary) at P, Q, X, Y, respectively.

Prove that the circles APQ and HXY have equal radius.

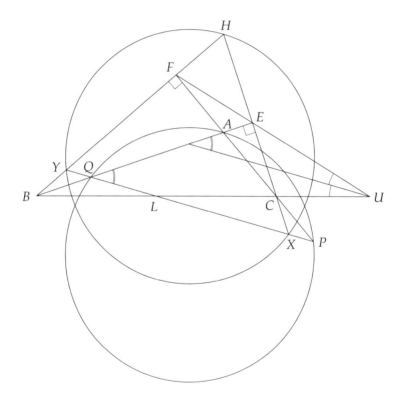

Problem H 2

The triangle ABC has orthocentre H. The altitude BH meets the perpendicular at C to BC at X; the altitude CH meets the perpendicular at B to BC at Y. The midpoints of CX and BY are X^* and Y^*, respectively.

Prove that X^*Y^* passes through H and is perpendicular to the median through A, meeting that median at U, say. Show that U lies on the circle BHC and that circle AUB touches BC at B.

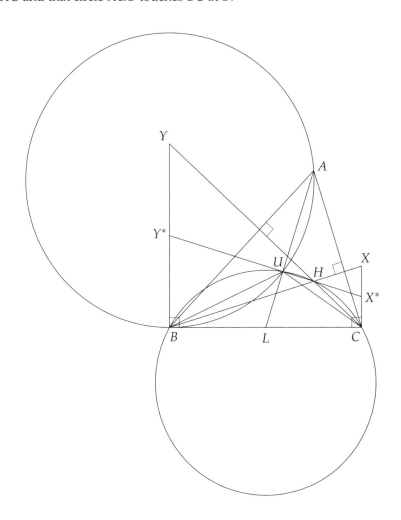

Problem H 3

Two circles meet at A and B. The tangent at a point P of one of the circles meets the other circle at Q and R. The points X, Y, Z are the feet of the perpendiculars from P to AB, AQ, BR respectively.

Prove that circle XYZ passes through the midpoint M of AB.

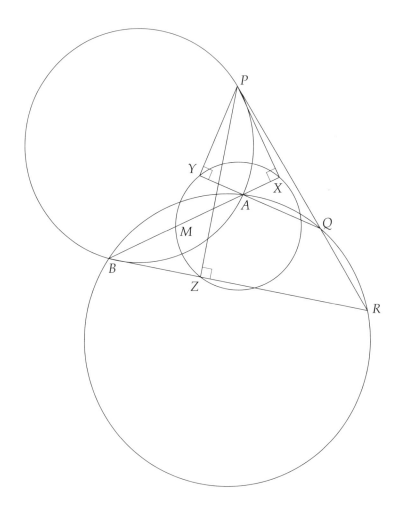

Problem H 4

The triangle ABC is acute-angled and $AC < BC$. The circumcentre is O and the orthocentre is H; the altitude CH meets AB at F. The perpendicular to OF at F meets AC at P.

Prove that $\angle FHP = \angle BAC$.

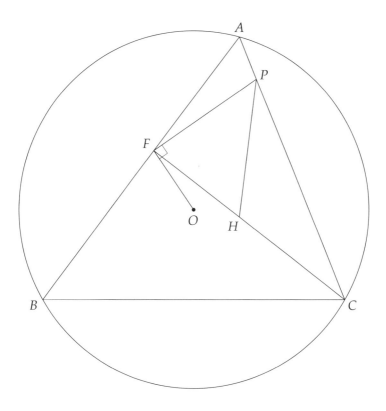

Problem H 5

The acute-angled triangle ABC has circumcentre O and orthocentre H. The perpendicular bisector of BH meets AB at Q, the perpendicular bisector of CH meets AC at P and these two bisectors meet at R.

(a) Prove that the circumcircles AOP, POR, ROQ, QOA have equal radii. When are they equal in radius to the circumcircle of ABC?

(b) Prove that if PQ passes through O then it also passes through H. What can be said about $\angle BAC$ in this case?

(c) Suppose circles AOP and ROQ meet again at S. What can be said about circle PRS?

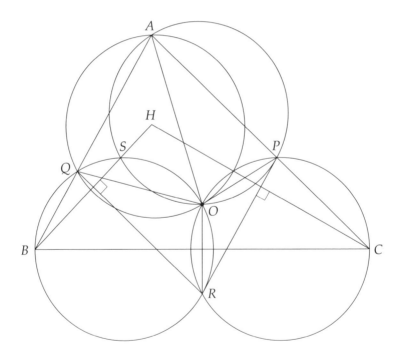

Problem H 6

The points P and Q are distinct points on the side BC of triangle ABC. The points K and L are the feet of the perpendiculars from P and Q, respectively, to the line AC. The points M and N are on the line AB such that $PM = PA$ and $QN = QA$. None of the points K, L, M, N coincides with A. It is given that the circles AKM and ALN meet again at R, the midpoint of BC.

Find the ratios $BC : CA$ and $CA : AB$.

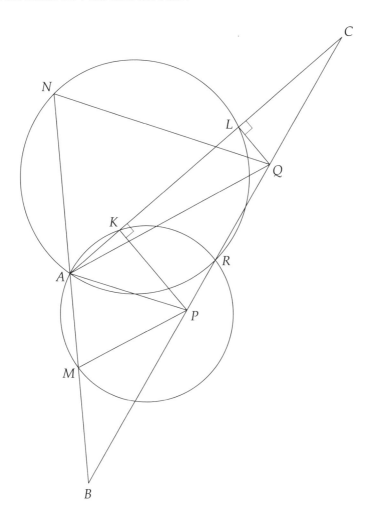

Problem H 7

The tangents at B and A to the circumcircle of the acute-angled triangle ABC meet the tangent at C at T and U respectively. Lines AT and BC meet at P, and Q is the midpoint of AP; lines BU and AC meet at R, and S is the midpoint of BR.

Prove that $\angle ABQ = \angle BAS$ and determine (in terms of ratios of side lengths) the triangles for which this angle is maximised.

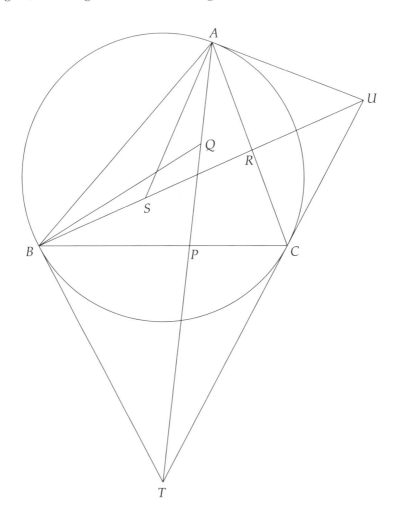

Problem H 8

The triangle ABC has an obtuse angle at B. The perpendiculars to CA and CB at C meet the side AB produced at P and Q, respectively. The midpoints of BP and PQ are R and S, respectively. It is given that $CB = CP$.

(a) Prove that $CA = CQ$.

(b) Prove that CR is the tangent at C to circle ABC.

(c) Let T be the point of contact of the other tangent from R to the circle. Show that CT is perpendicular to CS.

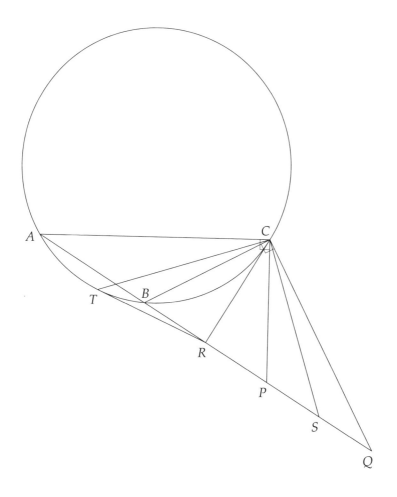

Problem H 9

The acute-angled triangle ABC has circumcentre O and orthocentre H. The altitude BH meets the circle ABC again at P and OP meets CA at Q; the altitude CH meets the circle again at R and OR meets AB at S.

Prove that the lines PQ, QH, HS, SR touch a circle.

What happens if $\angle BAC = 45°$?

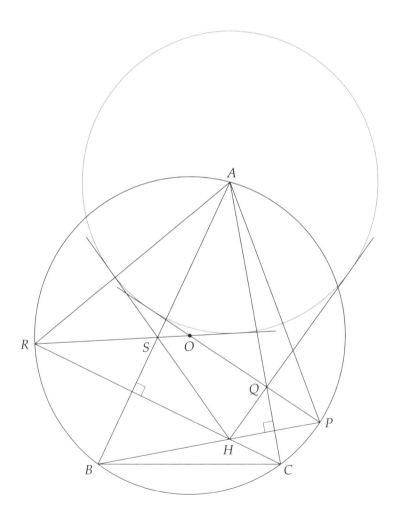

Problem H 10

The acute-angled triangle ABC has altitudes AD, BE, CF and orthocentre H. The tangents at B and C to circle ABC meet at T and they meet the line EF at X and Y respectively.

Identify the incentre of triangle XYT.

If L is the midpoint of BC prove that LH, DT, EF are concurrent.

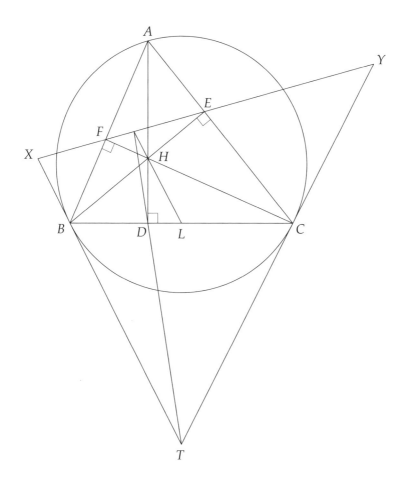

Problem H 11

The triangle ABC is right-angled at A. A line through the midpoint D of BC meets AB at X and AC at Y. The point P is taken on this line so that PD and XY have the same midpoint M. The perpendicular from P to BC meets BC at T.

Prove that AM bisects $\angle TAD$.

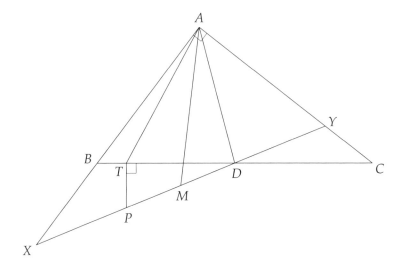

Problem H 12

The points D, E, F lie in order on the side BC of triangle ABC with $BD = DE = EF = FC$. The inscribed circle of the triangle touches BC at F. The lines DA, FA meet the perpendicular bisector of EF at X and Y.

Prove that the circle on XY as diameter passes through C.

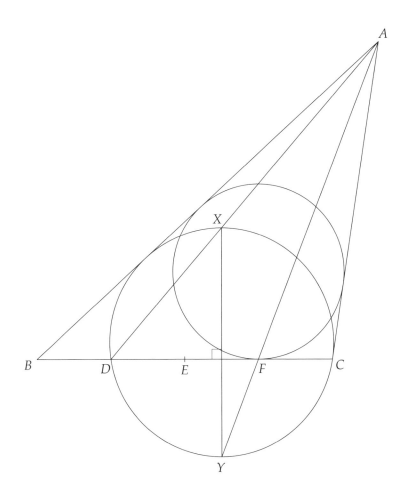

Problem H 13

In the acute-angled triangle ABC, the altitudes from B and C meet the opposite sides at E and F, respectively.

Prove that if $BF + CE = EF$ then the centre I of the inscribed circle of ABC lies on EF.

Show that the circumcircle of ABC and the escribed circle opposite A have the same radius R, and find the distance between their centres O and J in terms of R.

Find the minimum magnitude of $\angle BAC$ for such a triangle.

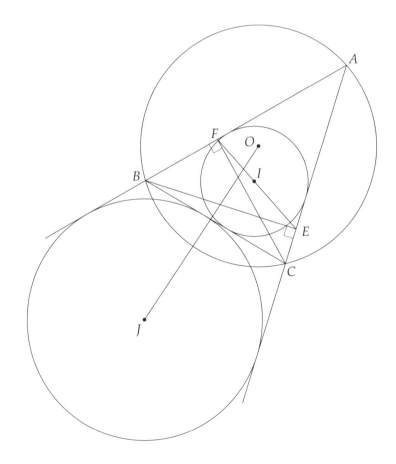

Problem H 14

The triangle ABC has centroid G. The point P is on BG produced such that $\angle PCG = \angle BAC$ and PQ is drawn perpendicular to CG.

Find the minimum value of $\dfrac{GC}{PQ}$.

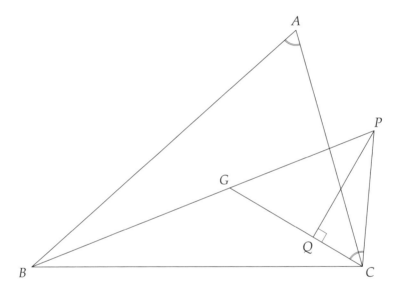

Problem H 15

A point O is outside a circle. Two lines OAB, OCD through O meet the circle at A, B, C, D with A, C the midpoints of OB, OD respectively. Also, the acute angle θ between the lines is equal to the acute angle at which each line cuts the circle. Thus $\angle OAP = \theta$, where AP is the tangent at A and $\angle OCT = \theta$, where CT is the tangent at C.

Find $\cos\theta$ and show that the tangents at A, D to the circle meet on the line BC.

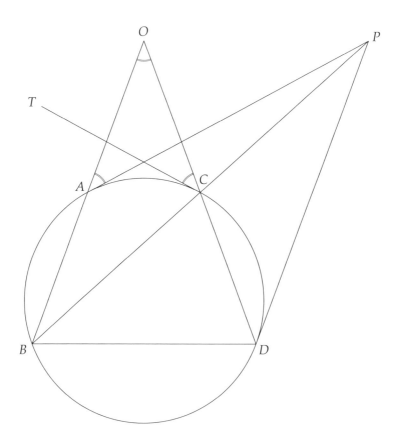

Problem H 16

The triangle ABC has orthocentre H, and P is a point not lying on its circumcircle. The perpendiculars from P to BC, CA, AB meet these lines at L, M, N, respectively. The point Q is the midpoint of PH.

Given that $QMLN$ is a parallelogram, determine the angles of ABC.

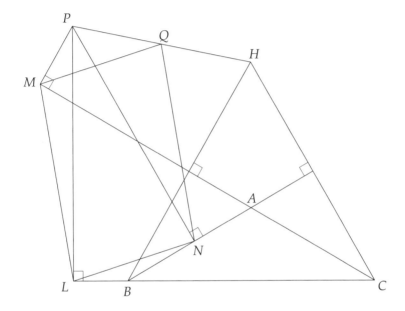

Problem H 17

In triangle ABC, the perpendicular bisectors of sides AB and AC meet the internal bisector of $\angle BAC$ at X and Y respectively.

Prove that if circle ACX touches BC at C and meets AB again at Z then $BZ = CA$ and circle ABY touches BC at B.

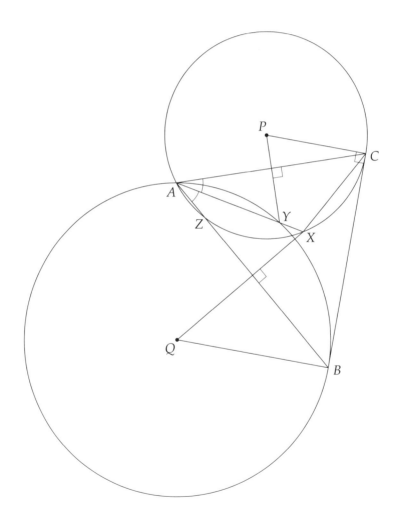

Problem H 18

The acute-angled triangle ABC has circumcentre O and $AODB$ is a parallelogram. The perpendicular from A to BC meets CD at X; the perpendicular from B to AC meets OC at Y.

Given that XY is parallel to AO find $\angle ABC$.

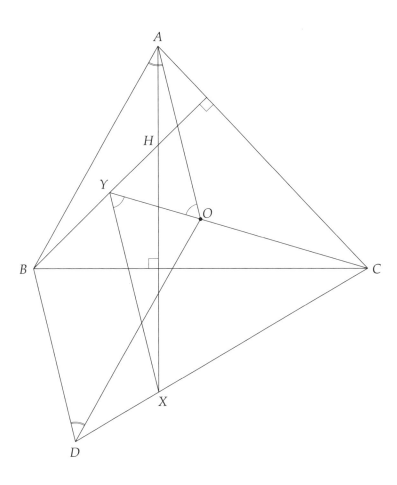

Chapter 4

Problems C

Problem C1

Triangle ABC is such that $\angle ACB > \angle BAC$. A variable point P lies on the arc BC of the circumcircle not containing A. The line AP meets BC at Q. The extension of BP meets the extension of AC at R.

Prove that

$$\frac{CA \times CR - CB \times CQ}{CQ \times CR}$$

is constant.

What is the relation of AB to the circle if this constant is zero?

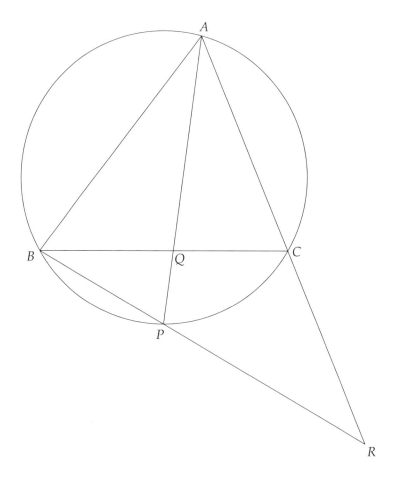

Problem C 2

The tangents at A and B to circle ABC meet at P.

Prove that the perpendicular bisector of BC and the line through P parallel to BC meet at a point on AC.

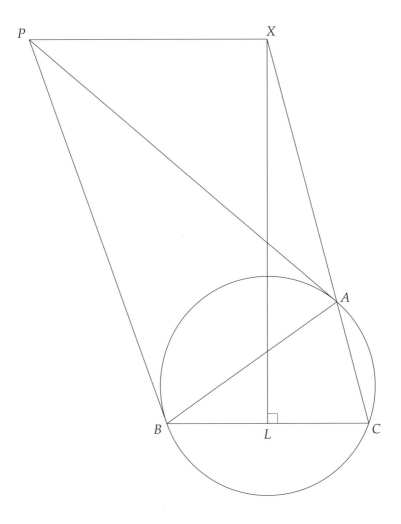

Problem C 3

The tangents at B and C to the circumcircle of triangle ABC meet at T. The midpoint of BC is L.

Given that $AT = 2AL$ find $\angle BAC$.

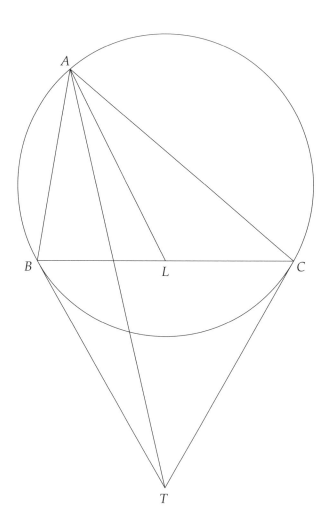

Problem C 4

The tangents at B and C to circle ABC meet at T. The line AT meets BC at U.

Given that $\angle BAC = 30°$ and $\angle AUC = 60°$ find the ratio $AB : AC$.

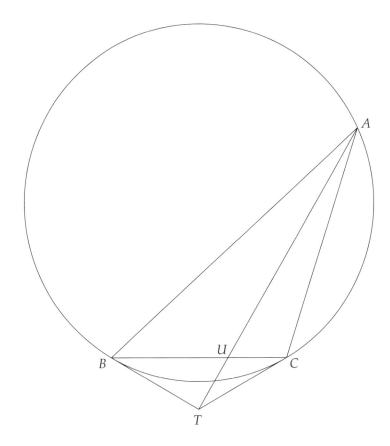

Problem C 5

ABCD is a quadrilateral. The lines *AD* and *BC* meet at *P*; the lines *AB* and *DC* meet at *Q*. It is immediate that if *ABCD* is cyclic then

$$\frac{PA \times PD}{QC \times QD} = \frac{PB \times PC}{QA \times QB}.$$

Is the converse true?

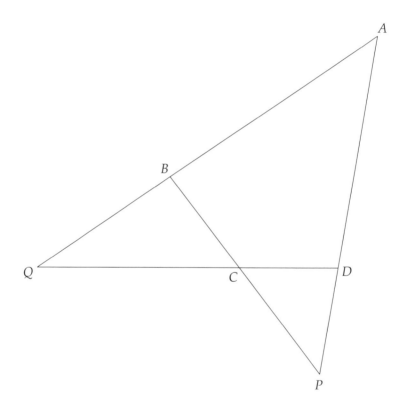

Problem C 6

In triangle ABC the circumcentre is O and the orthocentre is H. The perpendicular bisector of AH meets the side CA at P and the line OP meets the side BC at Q.

Prove that triangle QPC is isosceles.

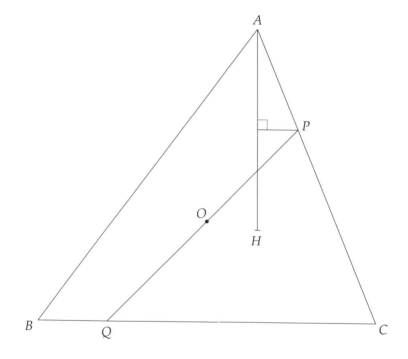

Problem C 7

In triangle ABC, the point D is on the line BC such that $4BD = DC$. The line AD meets the circumcircle of ABC again at E. The point F is the midpoint of CE.

Given that $\angle EAF = 45°$ find the angles of triangle ABC.

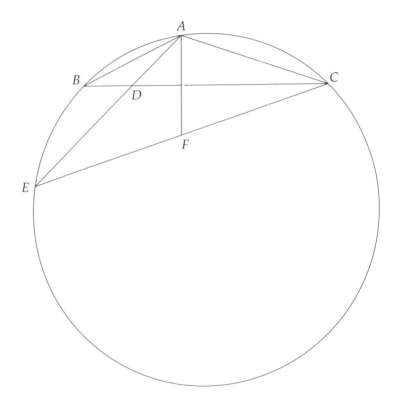

Problem C 8

Triangle ABC has centroid G and N is the foot of the perpendicular from G to BC. Consider those triangles with $AB \neq AC$ for which AN is the internal bisector of $\angle BAC$.

Prove that for all such triangles the ratio $BN : BA$ has the same value, which should be determined.

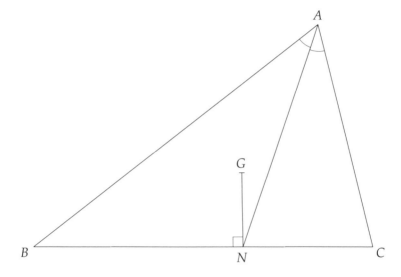

Problem C 9

The triangle ABC is equilateral. The point D lies on the line through A perpendicular to BC and is on the same side of BC as A. The point E lies on the opposite side of the line AD from B and $AE = ED = BD$.

Find $\angle CBE$.

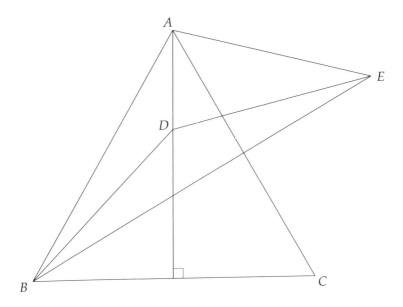

Problem C 10

In triangle ABC, the point L is the midpoint of BC and BE is the altitude from B to CA.

Given that $\angle BAL = 45°$ find the minimum value of $\dfrac{CA}{BE}$ and the magnitude of $\angle BAC$ in a triangle for which the minimum is attained.

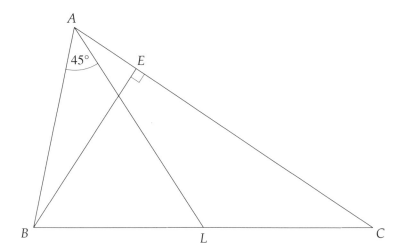

Problem C 11

The triangle ABC has circumcentre O and $\angle A$ is acute. The line OC is extended to D so that $OC = CD$. The points E, F, G are the feet of the perpendiculars from B, C, A to the lines CA, AB, OD, respectively.

Given that $2CA + EF = 2DG$ find the angles of the triangle.

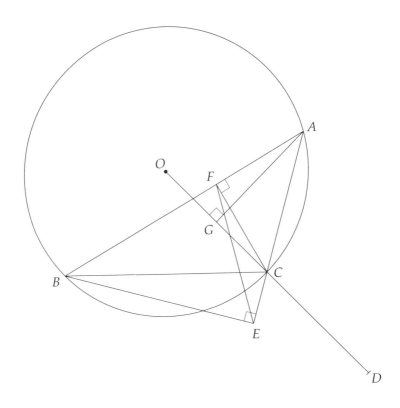

Problem C 12

In the quadrilateral $ABCD$, the sides AD and BC are not parallel. The diagonals AC and BD meet at E. The points F and G divide AB and DC respectively in the ratio $AD : BC$.

Prove that if E, F, G are collinear then A, B, C, D are concyclic.

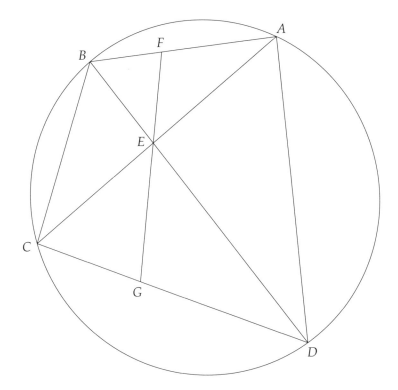

Problem C 13

The quadrilateral $ABCD$ has $\angle CAB = 50°$, $\angle DBC = 20°$, $\angle ACD = 40°$ and $\angle BDA = 70°$.

Find the angle between the diagonals AC and BD.

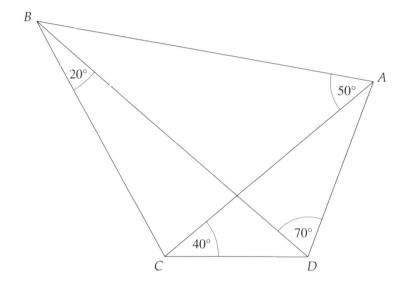

Problem C 14

In the cyclic quadrilateral $ABCD$, the diagonals AC and BD meet at X. The midpoints of AB and CD are E and F, respectively.

Prove that if $\angle AFD = \angle CEB$ then $\angle XFC = \angle ABC$.

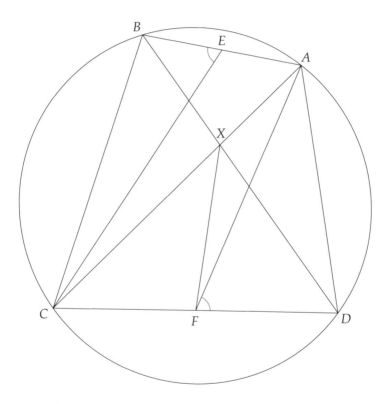

Problem C 15

In the quadrilateral $ABCD$, the lines AD and BC meet at P. The line ℓ passes through P and is parallel to AB. The perpendicular distances of C, D from ℓ and of P from CD are p, q and r, respectively.

Prove that if $ABCD$ is cyclic then $pq = r^2$.

Is the converse true?

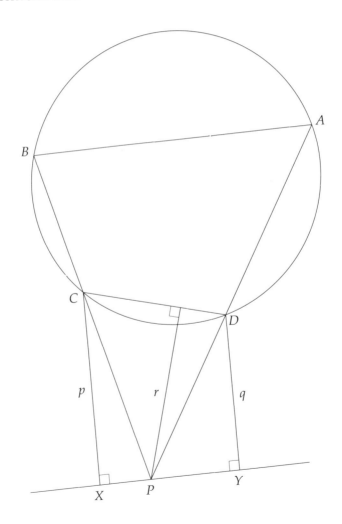

Problem C 16

The inscribed circle of triangle ABC touches BC, CA, AB at P, Q, R respectively. The line through A parallel to QR meets the line PQ at X.

Prove that BX passes through the midpoint M of QR.

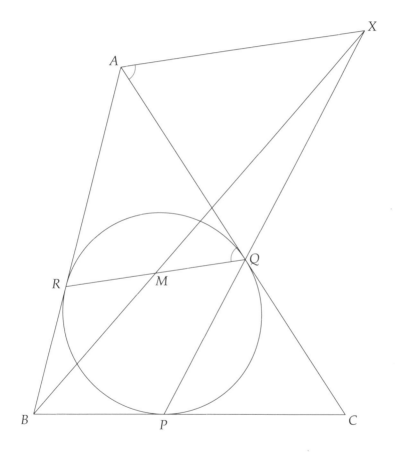

Problem C 17

In the cyclic quadrilateral $ABCD$, the sides BA, CD produced meet at P. The points E and F are the midpoints of AB and CD, respectively.

Given that $PD = DC$ and $\angle DBC = 30°$ find $\angle AEF$.

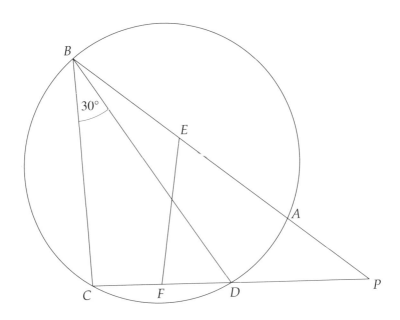

Problem C 18

In the cyclic quadrilateral $ABCD$, the diagonals AC and BD meet at E. The points M and N are the midpoints of AB and AC respectively. The lines CM and AD meet at P; the lines DN and BC meet at Q.

Given that PQ is parallel to AB, find the ratio $AE : EC$.

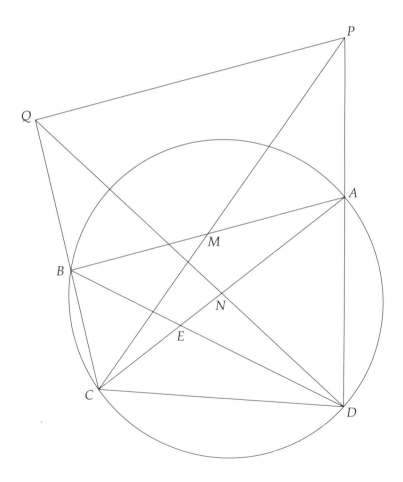

Problem C 19

Triangle ABC is equilateral. The point D is the midpoint of BC and DB is extended to E so that $EB = BD$. The point X is on the side AB and Y is taken on the extension of BA so that $XY = BA$. The lines EX and DY meet at Z.

Prove that $\angle ZCE = 2\angle ZEC$.

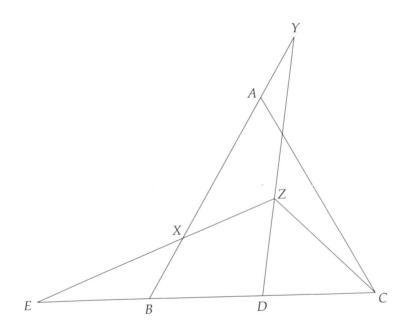

Problem C 20

Two circles C and D, of radii a and b respectively, touch externally at the point A. Points P on C and Q on D are such that $\angle PAQ = 120°$ and the tangents at P and Q intersect on the internal bisector of that angle.

Determine the ratio $AP : AQ$ in terms of a and b.

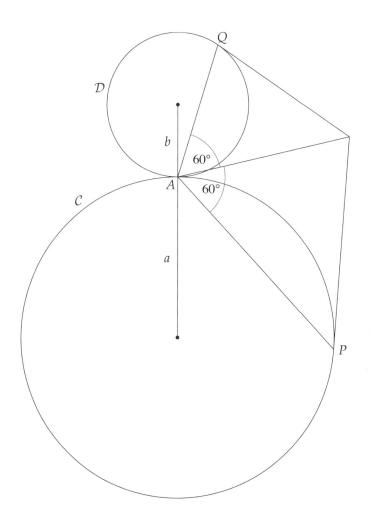

Problem C 21

The triangle ABC, in which AB and AC are unequal, has orthocentre H and L is the midpoint of BC. The perpendiculars to BC and HL at L meet AB at X and Y respectively.

Prove that $AX = BY$.

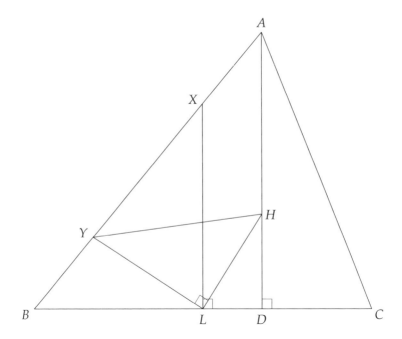

Problem C 22

The acute-angled triangle ABC has circumcentre O and orthocentre H. The line through H parallel to CA meets BA at X and the line through H parallel to BA meets CA at Y.

Prove that triangle OXY is isosceles and determine its angles in terms of $\angle A$.

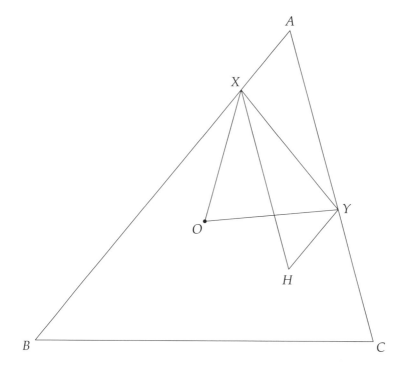

Problem C 23

The altitudes through A, B, C of triangle ABC meet the opposite sides at D, E, F, respectively. The line through D parallel to EF meets the lines AC, AB at Q, R, respectively, and EF meets BC at P.

Prove that the circle PQR passes through L, the midpoint of BC.

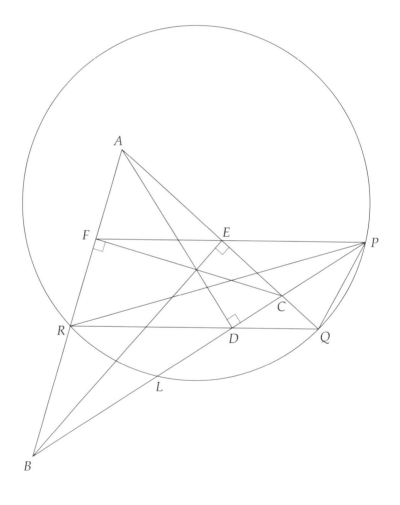

Problem C 24

Triangle PAB has $\angle PBA = 2\angle PAB$. The point C is on the side AB such that $AC = 2CB$. Parallel lines ℓ and m through A and C respectively are inclined at an angle of $60°$ to AB. The line PC meets ℓ at Q and AP meets m at R.

Show that QR is perpendicular to AB.

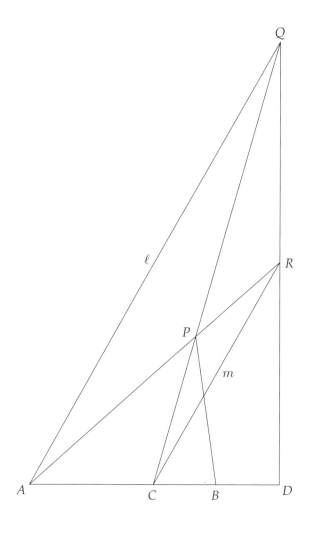

Chapter 5

Problems T

The following problems relate to a triangle ABC, with side lengths denoted by a, b, c, circumradius R and area $[ABC]$. The circumcentre is O and the orthocentre H.

T1. If $2\cos A\cos B(1+\cos C)=1$, find A, B and C.

T2. If $c=2b$, find the minimum value of $\cot B-\cot C$.

T3. If $6[ABC]=2a^2+bc$, find A, B and C.

T4. Prove that $3a^2+3b^2-c^2\ge 4\sqrt{3}[ABC]$.

T5. Prove that $b^2+c^2+R^2\ge a^2$ and specify the triangles for which equality occurs.

T6. Given that $4R=(b+c)(1-2\cos A)$, find A, B and C.

T7. Given that $a^2+b^2+c^2-4\sqrt{3}[ABC]=2R^2$, what can be said about A, B and C?

T8. For points P other than A, define

$$F(P)=\frac{BP^2+CP^2}{AP^2}.$$

If there are three distinct points Q, R and S on BC such that $F(Q)=F(R)=F(S)$, find A, B and C and the common value of F.

T9. If D divides BC in the ratio $2:1$, $\angle ADB=60°$ and $C=45°$, find A and B.

T10. Given that $a\ge b\ge c$, suppose that x, y, z are real numbers, not all zero, such that

$$\left(a^2x+b^2y+c^2z\right)^2=3b^2c^2(yz+zx+xy).$$

Find A, B, C and all possible triples (x,y,z).

T11. Let ABC be acute-angled, and, for an interior point P, let u, v, w be the perpendicular distances of P from BC, CA and AB.

Prove that $avw+bwu+cuv$ has maximum value $\frac{1}{4}abc$ when P is at O.

T12. If ABC is acute-angled, and $5R^2=OH^2+4[ABC]$, find the smallest angle of the triangle.

T13. The point P lies on BC, Q on AC produced beyond C and R on AB produced beyond B. The perpendicular distances of P from CA and AB are p_1, p_2; those of Q from AB and BC are q_1, q_2; those of R from BC and CA are r_1, r_2.

If $a^2 q_2 r_1 = b^2 r_2 p_1 = c^2 p_2 q_1 = \lambda$, show that $\lambda = 4[ABC]^2$ and prove that AP, BQ and CR are concurrent.

T14. Let ABC be acute-angled, and let P and Q vary on AB, AC in such a way that

$$\frac{AP}{PB} = \frac{CQ}{QA}.$$

Prove that there is a fixed point F in the interior of ABC such that $\frac{FP}{FQ}$ is a constant, and determine whether there is any other fixed point in the plane of the triangle with that property.

T15. Let P be a point inside ABC, and AP, BP, CP meet BC, CA, AB at L, M, N, respectively.

Find the position of P for which

$$\left(\frac{AP}{AL}\right)^2 + \left(\frac{BP}{BM}\right)^2 + \left(\frac{CP}{CN}\right)^2$$

is a minimum.

T16. Let D divide BC internally in the ratio $1 : 2$, and let E divide AD externally in the ratio $2 : -1$.

If $C = 2B$, prove that $\angle ECB + 180° = 2\angle EBC$.

T17. The circumcircle of triangle ABC is $\mathcal{K}$. For a point P, let

$$F(P) = AP \times BP + AP \times CP - BP \times CP.$$

There are three distinct points Q, R and S lying between B and C on that arc of $\mathcal{K}$ which does not contain A, such that $F(Q) = F(R) = F(S)$.

Prove that ABC is equilateral.

T18. For P a point in the plane of ABC, let L, M and N be the feet of the perpendiculars from P to BC, CA and AB, respectively.

Prove that there is a unique point U in the plane of ABC with the property that there exist real numbers s, t, u, v, not all zero, such that

$$sPL^2 + tPM^2 + uPN^2 + vUP^2$$

is constant for all P, and identify it.

Hints for solution

Problems E

E1. Consider quadrilateral $NGLB$, where G is the centroid.

E2. $ADBT$ is cyclic.

E3. Consider quadrilateral $XECY$.

E4. Start with $\angle ACQ = \angle ACP + \angle PCQ$.

E5. $\angle PQT = \angle ABC$ and $UQTP$ is cyclic. Note that the condition that AB is not parallel to CD ensures that the argument does not collapse.

E6. Prove that $QAHR$ is cyclic and hence triangles ARQ and CBA are similar.

E7. Triangle PAB is isosceles, so P lies on the perpendicular bisector of AB, that is $PO \perp AB$. Prove that $XOEQ$ is cyclic, where X is the intersection of OP and AB, and hence BO is perpendicular to PQ.

E8. Show triangle AHO is isosceles and use the fact that $AH = 2OA'$, where A' is the midpoint of BC.

E9. $\angle YIB = \frac{1}{2}\angle B + \frac{1}{2}\angle C = 90° - \frac{1}{2}\angle A = \angle AQY$, since triangle PAQ is isosceles. Hence $QYIB$ is cyclic and $\angle BYI = 90°$. Similarly $\angle CXI = 90°$. So C, B, X, Y are concyclic; the centre of the circle is the midpoint of BC.

E10. Let X be the intersection of HA and PC and Y be the intersection of HC and AR. Label $\angle QHA = \alpha$, $\angle SHC = \beta$ and use intersecting chords to show that

$$HP \times HQ \cos^2 \alpha = HX \times HA = HY \times HC = HR \times HS \cos^2 \beta.$$

E11. Deduce from the cyclic quadrilateral $AEPF$ that $EF = AP \sin A$. Hence show that the expression is equal to $\frac{[ABC]}{R}$.

E12. Use the tangent-secant form of the intersecting chord theorem to change the expression to one involving OA and R.

E13. Prove that $\angle CAB = \angle PCQ$, using the facts that $PSAR$ and $PQRC$ are cyclic.

For the second part note that $[PQRS] = 2[PQR]$, then using similar triangles you can prove $AC = 2PR$.

E14. Triangles ACQ and DBQ are similar. Use the sine rule on triangles ARB and DBQ. For the final question use the sine rule again.

E15. Prove that $\angle XZY = \angle XMY$ noting the cyclic quadrilaterals $DZYP$ and $DXRZ$. Also $\angle XMC = 2\angle XDC$ and $\angle CMY = 2\angle CDY$.

E16. Join NT and TL. Use the fact that N is the centre of circle PTR and L the centre of circle QTS to prove that $\angle NTL = 180° - \angle B$.

E17. The key to this is provided by the figure, which suggests that X, Y, Z are collinear with D. Take D to be on the minor arc AC. Let DX meet AB in Z_0 and CA in Y_0. Let $\angle DXP = \angle DPX = \theta$, then prove $\angle DZ_0R = \angle DRZ_0 = 60° - \theta$, so Z_0 coincides with Z. Similarly $\angle DY_0Q = \angle DQY_0 = 60° + \theta$, so Y_0 coincides with Y.

E18. *Either:* let AU meet BC at L. Use the intersecting chord theorem to show that L is the midpoint of BC. Show that $\angle BUL = \angle B$ and $\angle CUL = \angle C$. Bring in the angles θ, ϕ that BU, CU make with the common tangent at U and find two independent equations satisfied by $\angle A$, $\angle B$, $\angle C$, $\theta + \phi$ to provide the solution.

Or: let the given common tangent at U meet AB at V and AC at W. Then $\angle VBU = \angle VUB$, $\angle UBC = \angle BAU$ and two similar results. Now use $\angle VUB + \angle BUC + \angle CUW = 180°$.

Problems M

M1. Let H be the midpoint of BG so that FH is parallel to GC. Prove that triangles FHG, FED are similar.

M2. Use Cartesian coordinates. Take $\mathcal{C}$ and $\mathcal{C}^*$ to have equations

$$x^2 + y^2 - 2ax - 1 = 0 \quad \text{and} \quad x^2 + y^2 - 2bx - 1 = 0.$$

Suppose P has coordinates (X, Y). Show $\mathcal{S}_P$ has equation

$$x^2 + y^2 - 2Xx - 2Yy + 2aX + 1 = 0.$$

Now find the common chord of $\mathcal{S}_P$ and $\mathcal{C}^*$ and put in the condition that it passes through P. You should find the locus of P is the circle $\mathcal{K}$ with equation

$$x^2 + y^2 - (a + b)x - 1 = 0.$$

$\mathcal{K}$ has real points, is coaxal with $\mathcal{C}$ and $\mathcal{C}^*$ and is symmetrical under the interchange of a and b.

M3. Translate the circumcircle of ABC through the vector $\mathbf{BA}$, considering the point diametrically opposite to A.

M4. Use Cartesian coordinates with A as origin and the internal and external bisectors of $\angle BAC$ as the x- and y-axes, respectively.

M5. *Either:* let N be the midpoint of AB so that LN is parallel to CA. Then show that triangles AXM and NLA are similar. You should get

$$\frac{AX}{AM} = \frac{b}{c} \quad \text{and} \quad \frac{BX}{CF} = \frac{b^2 + 2c^2}{2bc \sin A},$$

with a minimum of $\sqrt{2}$ when $A = 90°$ and $b = c\sqrt{2}$.

Or: find AX by using the sine rule on triangle AXM; obtain the ratio $\sin \angle BAL : \sin \angle LAC$ by equating the areas $[ABL]$ and $[ALC]$.

M6. *Either:* We have to prove $\angle TH'O' = 90°$. Look for parallelograms. Consider the orthocentre of triangle ALT, where L is the midpoint of BC.

Or: Use complex numbers to show that $\frac{H'O'}{H'T}$ is purely imaginary.

M7. Use coordinates with O as origin, OA as x-axis and the circle as $x^2 + y^2 = a^2$.

M8. Note $SA = SP$ and $TB = TQ$. Use the sine rule for triangles PUS and QVT. Let QT meet ℓ at Y. Note that $\frac{AY}{AS} = \frac{BW}{BT}$. Consider triangles QXO, QUY, where O is the centre of the circle.

$$BV : BT = 1 : 2,\ BW : BT = 1 : 3,\ AX : AB = 1 : 4.$$

M9. Use coordinates with A as origin, the bisectors of $\angle BAC$ as axes. $B(b, mb)$ and $C(c, -mc)$.

M10. $\angle BEC = \angle ADC$. Find $BF : FE = 2 : 1$. Prove D is the centre of the circumcircle of ABC.

M11. Use a coordinate system with an axis along DB.

M12. (a) Prove that $\angle PLQ = 180° - \angle PMQ$.

(b) You need the fact that if R is the intersection of AC and BD then OR is perpendicular to PQ (indeed O is the orthocentre of triangle PQR).

(c) If QK meets MP at N consider $MNKL$.

M13. Let AC, BD meet at Z. Then Z, P separate A, C harmonically (see page 112 of the Glossary). Prove that $EZ \times ZP = AZ \times ZC$. Look similarly at the line BD.

M14. Draw the perpendicular DE from D to AB. Consider $DEQP$.

M15. Start with $DQ \times QR = AQ \times QB$. Use similar triangles AQP, ABC.

M16. Use coordinates with

$$A\left(\frac{1 - a^2}{1 + a^2}, \frac{2a}{1 + a^2}\right),$$

and so on.

M17. Triangles PAB, PCD are similar. So too, therefore, are AXE, CYF, where E, F are the midpoints of AB, CD, respectively. For the converse, note there is another type of quadrilateral satisfying the condition, characterised by a relation between the sides AB, CD.

M18. Let A, B, C, D be the four points. To analyse the situation consider the partial figure resulting from the two choices AB and CD for k. It turns out that ℓ is the join of O to the centroid of (equal masses at) A, B, C, D.

M19. Use the sine rule to show that $\angle ATB = \angle ATC$ and deduce that $\angle CAT = \angle UAB$. It then follows that triangles ABT, CBU and ACT are all similar. From there, (a) is immediate and (b) follows from Ptolemy's theorem on quadrilateral $ACUT$.

M20. The most obvious method seems to be trilinear coordinates (see page 112 of the Glossary). It turns out that BX and CY are parallel to the tangent at A. This may also be proved by a cotangent calculation. Note that AT is the isogonal conjugate of AL (see page 112 of the Glossary). (AL passes through the centroid and AT passes through the symmedian point.)

Problems H

H1. Since $\angle YHX = 180° - \angle A$ it is sufficient to show that $PQ = XY$. Assuming, without loss of generality, that $\angle C > \angle B$ we have $\angle QLB = \frac{1}{2}(\angle C - \angle B)$ so $\angle AQL = \angle APL = 90° - \frac{1}{2}\angle A$. The sine rule now shows $BQ = CP$. Deduce that triangles BQY, CPX are congruent.

H2. Triangles HCX, ABC are similar, so HCX^*, ABL are similar and it follows that HX^* is perpendicular to AL. Similarly HY^* is perpendicular to AL.

For the second part, it is critical to see that LX^* is parallel to BX, from which $\angle X^*UC$ can be shown to be equal to $90° - \angle C$. It now follows that $\angle BUC = \angle BHC = \angle B + \angle C$.

For the final part show that $\angle Y^*UB = \angle A + \angle C$ and it is only one step from showing that $\angle UBL = \angle BAU$.

H3. Let AQ, BR meet at S. Show that the isogonal conjugate of P relative to triangle SAB lies on the perpendicular bisector of AB (see page 112 of the Glossary). This argument can be adapted to the case when AQ and BR are parallel.

H4. A trigonometrical calculation is possible. A proof can also be given by means of the famous butterfly theorem (see page 114 of the Glossary).

This problem was a proposal of mine for IMO 1996 and was short-listed. Consequently the problem appears in *The IMO Compendium* [3] on page 289 with solution on page 607.

H5. This is a good illustration of the advantages and dangers of an accurate figure. It suggests useful results, *but these must be proved.* Here circle QOR passes through B, circle POR through C and R is the reflection of O in BC. The common radius is $R \div (2\sin A)$.

H6. Let $PC = x$. Find the condition that $AKMR$ is cyclic; this is of first degree in x. If a second point has the same property the condition must be satisfied identically. Find that $a : b : c = \sqrt{6} : \sqrt{3} : 1$.

H7. Find that $\angle ABQ = \angle BAS = \theta$, where

$$\cot\theta = \frac{a^2 + b^2 + 3c^2}{4[ABC]}.$$

This has a minimum value $\sqrt{7}$ when $a : b : c = \sqrt{2} : \sqrt{2} : 1$ so the maximum value of θ is arctan $\frac{1}{\sqrt{7}}$.

This problem was submitted to IMO 2000 and shortlisted, so it appears in *The IMO Compendium* [3] on page 310 with solution on page 672.

H8. For parts (a), (b), use easy angle arguments. For part (c), if CT meets AB at U, then R, U separate A, B harmonically (see page 112 of the Glossary).

H9. A figure suggests that the circle has centre A. The distance from A to OPQ can be found by considering $[OAP]$ and is $R \sin 2A$. Similarly for the distance of A from ORS. Note that QH is got from QP by reflection in CA. For $\angle A = 45°$, PQ, SR are the same line (through O).

H10. Again the figure is helpful and suggests that L is the incentre of triangle XYT. Show that the distance from L to TX, XY, YT is $\frac{1}{2}a \sin A$. Note that triangles DEF, TYX are similar and H is the incentre of triangle DEF.

H11. Quadrilateral $ADMT$ is cyclic.

H12. Once more the accurate diagram is very useful and points to an indirect approach. Prove that $c = b + \frac{1}{2}a$. Consider the circle (homothetic from A to the incircle), which touches AC at C and touches AB between A and B (see page 111 of the Glossary).

H13. The condition on the triangle is $\cos A = \cos B + \cos C$. The easiest way of seeing that I lies on EF is to use trilinear coordinates (see page 112 of the Glossary). Recall the formula for the exradius r_1 involving half-angles. Also $OJ^2 = R^2 + 2Rr_1$. Find that $\angle A \geq \cos^{-1}(\sqrt{3} - 1)$.

H14. Note that
$$\frac{GC}{PQ} = \cot A + \cot \angle PGC.$$
Use the cotangent rule (see page 113 of the Glossary) to prove that
$$\cot \angle PGC = \tfrac{1}{3}(2 \cot B + 2 \cot C - \cot A).$$
To see the minimum consider
$$(\cot A + \cot B + \cot C)^2 - 3(\cot B \cot C + \cot C \cot A + \cot A \cot B).$$

H15. Straightforward calculation gives $\cos\theta = \frac{3}{4}$. That the tangents at A, D meet on BC (that is, AD, BC are conjugate lines with respect to the circle) corresponds to the relation $AB \times CD = AC \times BD$ (the so-called 'harmonic quadrilateral').

This problem was a proposal of mine for IMO 1983. It appears in *The IMO Compendium* [3] on page 160 without a solution.

H16. Use of complex numbers seems to be the only feasible approach here. Find that $\angle A = 120°$, $\angle B = \angle C = 30°$.

H17. Straightforward calculation using the sine rule in triangle ACX shows that $a^2 = bc$.

H18. Let Z be the intersection of AX and CY. Apply the sine rule to triangle XYZ. This leads, after some involved trigonometry, to $\sin(B - C) = 2\cos B \sin(A - B)$ and the two possible solutions are $B = 60°$ or $120°$.

Other methods are possible, including use of coordinates with the circle as $x^2 + y^2 = 1$ and

$$A(1,0), \quad B\left(\frac{1 - b^2}{1 + b^2}, \frac{2b}{1 + b^2}\right), \quad C\left(\frac{1 - c^2}{1 + c^2}, \frac{2c}{1 + c^2}\right).$$

Problems C

C1. Let $\angle PAC = \theta$ and use the sine rule on triangles CAQ and CBR to show the expression reduces to $2\cos C$.

C2. Let X be the intersection of AC with the perpendicular bisector of BC. Join BX and mark all the angles that are equal to $\angle BCA = \angle C$. Note $\angle AXB = 2\angle C$. You should now see that P, A, X, B are concyclic. Another angle is now equal to $\angle C$.

Alternatively, $PB = \frac{c}{2\cos C}$, so the distance of P from BC is $\frac{c\sin A}{2\cos C} = \frac{1}{2}a\tan C$.

C3. Use Apollonius' theorem (see page 113 of the Glossary) and the cosine rule to obtain the two values $60°$ and $120°$.

C4. By marking angles at B, C, T and U it is easy to find $BU : UC$. A standard result, which is straightforward to prove, is that

$$BU : UC = AB^2 : AC^2.$$

C5. Use the sine rule. Two cases arise: there is a second type of quadrilateral that has the property.

C6. Calculate AP and hence PE, where E is the midpoint of AC. Find $\angle QPC$.

C7. Use the cotangent rule (see page 113 of the Glossary) to show that

$$5\alpha^2 + 6\alpha\beta + 2\beta^2 - 2\alpha - 2\beta + 1 = 0,$$

where $\alpha = \cot A$, $\beta = \cot B$. Regard this as a quadratic in α (with coefficients involving β) and complete the square.

C8. Find $BN = \frac{2}{3}(a - \frac{1}{2}b\cos C)$ and a similar expression for CN. Then manipulate

$$\frac{BN}{c} = \frac{CN}{b} = \frac{BN + CN}{b + c} = \frac{BN - CN}{c - b}$$

to get a simple equation for $\dfrac{a}{b + c}$. The answer is $1 : \sqrt{3}$.

C9. This is a straightforward calculation using Pythagoras' theorem. The answer is $30°$.

C10. $2\cot A + \cot B = 1$ and $\frac{CA}{BE} = \cot A + \cot C$. Express this as a rational function of $\cot A$. The answer is $2(\sqrt{2}-1)$ with $\angle BAC = 112\frac{1}{2}°$.

C11. Express the distances in terms of R, the circumradius, and functions of the angles. Show that

$$\left(\sin B - \tfrac{1}{2}\right)^2 + (\text{another non-negative expression}) = 0.$$

C12. Use Menelaus' theorem for triangles BCD and ABC (see page 114 of the Glossary). Dividing and using the fact that

$$\frac{DG}{GC} = \frac{AD}{BC} = \frac{AF}{FB}$$

we have

$$\frac{AD^2}{BC^2} = \frac{AE \times DE}{BE \times CE}. \qquad (*)$$

Now use the sine rule for triangles ADE and BCE and the resulting trigonometrical equation, after using (*), gives two possibilities, one of which must be rejected because AD is not parallel to BC.

Alternatively, a vector approach can be used.

C13. This can be solved by using the sine rule, but beware there is more than one answer. Find that $\angle BEC = 80°$ or $90°$ (in the latter case the quadrilateral is cyclic).

C14. Let $\angle ACD = \theta$ and $\angle BDC = \phi$, then $\cot \angle AFD = \frac{1}{2}(\cot \theta - \cot D)$ and $\cot \angle CEB = \frac{1}{2}(\cot \phi - \cot B)$ using the cotangent rule (see page 113 of the Glossary). Make a third application of the cotangent rule.

C15. $p = PC \sin B$, and so on. There are *two* similar expressions for r.

C16.

$$\frac{RM}{AX} = \frac{BR}{BA} = \frac{s-b}{c}.$$

Apply the sine rule to triangle AQX to find AX, using formulae such as

$$\cos \frac{B}{2} = \sqrt{\frac{s(s-b)}{ca}}.$$

C17. Work with cotangents. Find $\angle AEF = 60°$.

C18. $PQCD$ is cyclic so $\angle ADN = \angle BCM$. Now work with cotangents.

C19. Suppose the sides of triangle ABC have length 2 units. Take B as origin and let $\mathbf{i}$, $\mathbf{j}$ be unit vectors along BC and BA respectively. Note that $\mathbf{i} \cdot \mathbf{j} = \frac{1}{2}$. Let $BX = x\mathbf{j}$ $(0 < x < 2)$. Now calculate the position vector of Z. You should obtain

$$\mathbf{BZ} = \frac{1}{1+x}\,\mathbf{i} + \frac{x(x+2)}{1+x}\,\mathbf{j}.$$

Now calculate $ZC = b$, $ZE = c$ and with $EC = a = 3$ you should get $ab = c^2 - b^2$. This implies $\angle ZCE = 2\angle ZEC$.

C20. Trigonometrical calculations yield the rather improbable looking result

$$AP : AQ = a^{\frac{2}{3}} : b^{\frac{2}{3}}.$$

C21. *Either:* let $AB > AC$ and show $DL = R\sin(C - B)$. Now let $\theta = \angle LHD = \angle YLB$. Work out $\cot\theta$ from triangle HDL and then use the sine rule on triangle BYL to obtain

$$BY = \frac{R\sin(C - B)}{\cos B} = AX.$$

Or: take coordinates with D as origin and $A(0, a)$, $B(b, 0)$ and $C(c, 0)$. It is straightforward to show that H is $(0, -\frac{bc}{a})$. It now suffices to work out the x-coordinate of Y.

C22. *Either:* note that $AYHX$ is a parallelogram so HA bisects XY. Use the cotangent rule (see page 113 of the Glossary) to find $\cot XYH$. Now $AY = 2R\cot A\cos B$ and a simple calculation shows that $\angle XYH = \angle OYC$. This gives $\angle XYO$ and $\angle YXO$ can be found similarly.

Or: use coordinates with $A(0, 0)$, $B(2, 2v)$, $C(2, 2w)$, then H has coordinates $\big(2(1 + vw), 0\big)$ and O has coordinates $(1 - vw, v + w)$. This particular coordinate system is often useful when A plays a special role.

Or: use complex numbers on the unit circle for A, B and C and consider the modulus and argument of $\frac{X}{Y}$.

C23. *Either:* in order to prove that $PQLR$ is cyclic it is sufficient to prove that $RD \times DQ = LD \times DP$. Now LD and DP are easily found to be

$$\tfrac{1}{2}(c\cos B - b\cos C) \quad \text{and} \quad \frac{2bc\cos B\cos C}{c\cos B - b\cos C},$$

since $BD : DC = BP : CP$. To work out RD and DQ, let AD meet EF at X and use the fact that triangles AFX and ARD are similar, as are triangles AXE and ADQ. You need to use the sine rule for triangle AXE. Intermediate results are

$$\frac{AD}{AX} = \frac{\cos(C-B)}{\cos A} \quad \text{and} \quad EX = \frac{2R\sin C\cos C\cos A}{\cos(C-B)}.$$

Finally $DQ = R\sin 2C$ and $DR = R\sin 2B$.

Or (using a more advanced idea): Note that $BCFE$ is cyclic and triangles ECP, BRD and QCD are similar. Deduce that $DQ : PE = DC : CP$; use this and a similar relation to show $DQ \times DR = DB \times DC$. Now D, P separate B, C harmonically (see page 112 of the Glossary), so

$$\frac{2}{DP} = \frac{1}{DC} - \frac{1}{DB}$$

(in the figure as shown).

This problem was a proposal of mine for IMO 1997 and was short-listed. It appears in *The IMO Compendium* [3] on page 295 with solution on page 627.

C24. *Either:* it can be shown that $\tan\angle PCB = 3\cot\angle PAB$. Straightforward trigonometrical calculations then prove that the feet of the perpendiculars from Q and R to AB coincide.

Or: use Cartesian coordinates with A as origin and AB as x-axis. The equation of AP is $y = x\tan\theta$, where $\theta = \angle PAB$, and that of CR is $y = \sqrt{3}(x - 2a)$, with similar expressions for the equations of AQ and CP. It turns out that the x-coordinates of both Q and R are the same, equal to

$$\frac{6a}{3 - \sqrt{3}\tan\theta}.$$

Problems T

T1. $2\cos A \cos B = \cos(A - B) + \cos(A + B) \le 1 - \cos C$. Find that $C = 90°$ and $A = B = 45°$.

T2. Use the cosine rule for $\cos B$ and $\cos C$ and the sine rule in the form $bc \sin A = ca \sin B = ab \sin C$.

An alternative approach is: If L is the midpoint of BC then

$$\cot B - \cot C = 2 \cot \angle ALC.$$

For fixed B, C the locus of A is a circle. Consider the tangent from L to this circle.

The answer is $\frac{3}{2}$ when $A = 90°$.

T3. Use $[ABC] = \frac{1}{2} bc \sin A$ and the cosine rule for a^2. You also need to use $b^2 + c^2 \ge 2bc$. The equation $3 \sin A + 4\cos A = 5$ determines A. B and C are then determinate.

T4. Use $[ABC] = \frac{1}{2} ab \sin C$ and the cosine rule for $\cos C$. Express everything in terms of a, b, C to show the inequality is equivalent to $a^2 + b^2 \ge 2ab \sin(C - 30°)$.

T5. Use the cosine rule to show that what you have to prove is that $8 \cos A \sin B \sin C + 1 \ge 0$. This is trivial unless A is obtuse. When this is so put $A = \theta + 90°$ and then $B + C + \theta = 90°$ and the inequality becomes the standard inequality $\sin B \sin C \sin \theta \le \frac{1}{8}$. Equality is when $A = 120°$ and $B = C = 30°$.

To see the genesis of this problem prove (a particular case of a standard formula) that if D is such that $ACDB$ is a parallelogram and P is any point then

$$PB^2 + PC^2 - PA^2 = PD^2 + a^2 - b^2 - c^2.$$

Apply this with P at the circumcentre.

T6. Using trigonometrical formulae show that

$$\left(\cos \frac{3A}{2}\right)\left(\cos \frac{B - C}{2}\right) = -1.$$

The answer is $A = 120°$, $B = C = 30°$.

T7.
$$\tfrac{1}{2}\left(a^2 + b^2 + c^2 - 4\sqrt{3}\,[ABC]\right) = AX^2,$$

where X lies on the same side of BC as A and triangle XBC is equilateral. So the equation certainly holds if $A = 30°$; also it is symmetrical in a, b, c which gives two other possibilities. The conclusion is confirmed by expressing the equation as

$$\cos A \cos B \cos C - \sqrt{3}\sin A \sin B \sin C = -\tfrac{3}{4}$$

and considering

$$\left(\cos A - \sqrt{3}\sin A\right)\left(\cos B - \sqrt{3}\sin B\right)\left(\cos C - \sqrt{3}\sin C\right).$$

The answer is that at least one angle is equal to $30°$.

T8. Let $BP = x$, $CP = a - x$ and then work out AP^2 in terms of a, b, c, x. What happens now if $F(P) = F(x) = k$ has three solutions for x?

T9. Let $DC = x$ and $AD = y$. The sine rule for triangle ADC gives $3y^2 = 2b^2$. Now use the cosine rule for triangles ADB and ADC to give $c^2 = 6x^2$ and $y = x(1 + \sqrt{3})$. Finally use the sine rule for triangle ABD to give $A = 60°$ and $B = 75°$. Or work with cotangents.

T10. Complete the square, the first step of which is

$$\left(b^2 y - \tfrac{1}{2}c^2 z + \left(a^2 - \tfrac{3}{2}c^2\right)x\right)^2 + \cdots.$$

At the end you should get two squares plus

$$3\left(2a^2c^2 + 2a^2b^2 - b^2c^2 - a^4 - b^4 - c^4\right)x^2.$$

Now you have to see why this implies $a = b = c$.

T11. *Either:* use the method of Lagrange's undetermined multipliers (see page 113 of the Glossary) on the function

$$F(u, v, w) = avw + bwu + cuv - \lambda\left(au + bv + cw - 2[ABC]\right)$$

and λ turns out to be the circumradius R and $u = R\cos A$, etc.

Or: use a non-calculus method, considering

$$4\triangle^2(\tfrac{1}{4}abc - avw - bwu - cuv)$$
$$= \tfrac{1}{4}abc\{(au + bv\cos 2C + cw\cos 2B)^2 + \text{another square}\},$$

where $\triangle = [ABC] = \tfrac{1}{2}(au + bv + cw)$.

T12. Considering the power of H with respect to the circumcircle gives

$$OH^2 = R^2(1 - 8\cos A\cos B\cos C).$$

Consider $(\sin A - \cos A)(\sin B - \cos B)(\sin C - \cos C)$. That the *smallest* angle has been identified is because the triangle is given to be acute-angled.

T13. $bp_1 + cp_2 = 2[ABC]$ and two similar equations hold. You may find it helpful to make the substitution $x = br_2$, $y = cp_2$, $z = -aq_2$ and consider the three equations

$$\frac{k}{x} + y = w, \quad \frac{k}{y} + z = w, \quad \frac{k}{z} + x = w,$$

where $w = 2[ABC]$ and k is the common product. Not only does the value of k emerge, but you also find $p_1q_1r_1 = p_2q_2r_2$, which with the aid of Ceva's theorem (see page 114 of the Glossary) establishes that AP, BQ, CR are concurrent.

T14. Consider particular points for P, Q, when for example P is at A, B and the midpoint of AB. You should find as a result that the constant must equal $\frac{c}{b}$ so that

$$\frac{FP}{FQ} = \frac{c}{b} = \frac{FB}{FA} = \frac{FA}{FC}.$$

If $b = c$, this means that F lies at the intersection of two lines, but if $b \neq c$, then F lies at the intersection of two Apollonius circles (see page 115 of the Glossary). When the triangle is acute-angled one of these points is internal. But even if this point is identified, an argument involving similar triangles is needed to show that it works for all possible pairs P, Q. Also when $b \neq c$, there is a second position of F lying on BC, dividing BC externally in a ratio which should be determined.

T15. Use areal coordinates with $P(l, m, n)$ (see page 111 of the Glossary). Each of l, m, n is positive, since P is an internal point. The given expression equals $(m + n)^2 + (n + l)^2 + (l + m)^2$. Using $l + m + n = 1$, this comes to $1 + l^2 + m^2 + n^2$. This is minimised when P is at the centroid.

T16. By taking the diameter of the circumcircle as unit of length we have $BC = \sin 3B$, $CA = \sin B$, $AB = \sin 2B$. Straightforward trigonometric calculations show that $\tan \angle EBC = -3 \cot B$ and the angle relation can be verified.

T17. Express $F(P)$ in terms of $\theta = \angle BAP$, so that $AP = 2r \sin(C + \theta)$ etc., where r is the circumradius. Suppose $F(Q) = F(R) = F(S) = 4r^2 k$. Obtain a quadratic equation in $t = \tan \theta$ which has three distinct roots corresponding to Q, R, S. Equating its coefficients to zero deduce that $\sin C - \sin A = \sin(C - A)$ and $\cos C + \cos A = \cos(C - A)$.

T18. Consider P on the sides to find that one must have (to within a non-zero multiplier) $s = \sin 2A$, $t = \sin 2B$, $u = \sin 2C$, $v = -2 \sin A \sin B \sin C$. The point U is the orthocentre.

This problem was a submission of mine for IMO 1989. It appears in *The IMO Compendium* [3] on page 234 with no solution.

Glossary

Definitions

Homothety   Triangles ABC and $A_1B_1C_1$ are homothetic if they are similar but not congruent, and corresponding sides are parallel. Homothetic triangles have the property that AA_1, BB_1 and CC_1 are concurrent at a point O called the centre of similitude, and O is the centre of an enlargement which maps ABC to $A_1B_1C_1$. If the scale factor is positive, this is a direct centre of similitude, and if the scale factor is negative, it is an inverse centre.

Areal coordinates   Given any triangle ABC, the point P has areal coordinates (x, y, z) if

$$x = \frac{[PBC]}{[ABC]}, \quad y = \frac{[PCA]}{[ABC]}, \quad z = \frac{[PAB]}{[ABC]}.$$

In other words, the coordinates represent the areas of the three triangles, normalised by the area of the original triangle, so that $x + y + z = 1$.

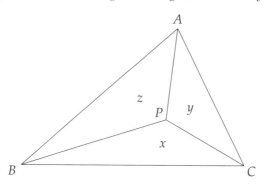

Unnormalised areal coordinates are sometimes called *barycentric coordinates*. There is a short discussion of areal coordinates in [1, 2, 4].

Trilinear coordinates Given any triangle ABC, the point P has trilinear coordinates (ka', kb', kc') if they are proportional to the perpendicular distances from P to the sides of the triangle, as shown in the diagram.

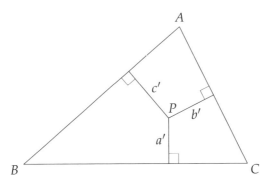

If $k = 1$, so that the coordinates represent the actual perpendicular distances, then they are called *exact* trilinears.

Trilinears are discussed in [2] and are used extensively in [5], where there is a clear explanation of their properties.

Isogonal conjugate The isogonal conjugate of a point X with respect to a triangle ABC is found by reflecting the lines AX, BX and CX in the internal angle bisectors of the triangle. It turns out these these lines are also concurrent at a point X^*, which is the isogonal conjugate of X.

For example, the orthocentre and circumcentre are isoogonal conjugates. If the trilinear coordinates of X are (α, β, γ), then the trilinear coordinates of X^* are $\left(\frac{1}{\alpha}, \frac{1}{\beta}, \frac{1}{\gamma}\right)$.

Harmonic range Let the line segment AB be divided internally by C and externally by D in the same ratio. In other words

$$\frac{AC}{CB} = -\frac{AD}{DB}.$$

Then A, C, B, D are said to form a harmonic range, or, alternatively, C and D divide AB harmonically. It turns out that, if this is the case, then $D, B,$

C, A is also a harmonic range, and B and A divide DC harmonically. If O is the midpoint of AB, then $OB^2 = OC \times OD$.

Lagrange multipliers   Lagrange multipliers are used to evaluate maxima and minima of a function $f(x_1, \ldots, x_n)$ of several variables where one or more exact constraints $g_i(x_1, \ldots, x_n) = 0$ have to be satisfied. A new function $L = f + \sum \lambda_i g_i$ is constructed, then the partial derivatives of L with respect to $x_1, \ldots, x_n$ and each λ_i are calculated. The stationary points are found by solving a set of simultaneous equations obtained by setting each derivative equal to zero.

Standard results

Cotangent rule   *In the triangle ABC, if L is the midpoint of BC, then*

$$\cot B - \cot C = 2 \cot \angle ALC.$$

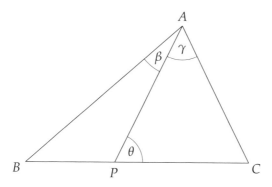

More generally, if P divides BC in the ratio $m : n$ and angles θ, β and γ are as shown above, then

$$n \cot B - m \cot C = (m + n) \cot \theta$$
$$m \cot \beta - n \cot \gamma = (m + n) \cot \theta$$
$$m \cot \beta = (m + n) \cot A + n \cot B.$$

Apollonius' theorem   *If ABC is a triangle, with median AL, then*

$$AB^2 + AC^2 = 2AL^2 + 2BL^2.$$

Ceva's theorem *Suppose the points L, M and N lie respectively on the sides BC, CA and AB of triangle ABC.*

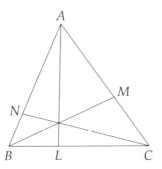

Then the lines AL, BM and CN are concurrent if, and only if,

$$\frac{BL}{LC} \times \frac{CM}{MA} \times \frac{AN}{NB} = 1.$$

Menelaus' theorem *Suppose the points L, M and N lie respectively on the sides BC, CA and AB of triangle ABC.*

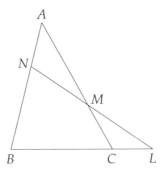

Then L, M and N are collinear if, and only if,

$$\frac{BL}{LC} \times \frac{CM}{MA} \times \frac{AN}{NB} = -1.$$

Butterfly theorem *Let Q, R be points on a circle and let S be the midpoint of QR. If XY, ZT are two chords of the circle through S, then XT and YZ meet QR at points equidistant from S.*

Apollonius circle *Let A and B be fixed points and let λ be a constant, not equal to 1. Then the locus of points P such that*

$$\frac{PA}{PB} = \lambda$$

is a circle.

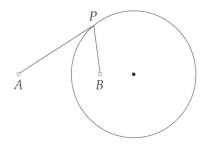

Bibliography

[1] Christopher J Bradley. *Challenges in Geometry: for Mathematical Olympians Past and Present*. Oxford University Press, 2005.

[2] Christopher J Bradley. *The Algebra of Geometry: Cartesian, Projective and Areal co-ordinates*. Highperception, 2007.

[3] Dušan Djukić, Vladimir Z Janković, Ivan Matić, and Nikola Petrović. *The IMO Compendium: A Collection of Problems Suggested for The International Mathematical Olympiads: 1959-2004*. Problem Books in Mathematics. Springer, 2006.

[4] A D Gardiner and C J Bradley. *Plane Euclidean Geometry*. The United Kingdom Mathematics Trust, 2005.

[5] Clark Kimberling. Encyclopedia of triangle centers – ETC [online]. October 2008. Available from: http://faculty.evansville.edu/ck6/encyclopedia/ETC.html.